Sunshine and Joy's

Big Book
of
Alzheimer's Activities

Volume 1

A treasury of armchair activities to spark the mind.

By Jill Hernandez

Published by Sunshine and Joy Enterprises

SUNSHINE AND JOY'S BIG BOOK OF ALZHEIMER'S ACTIVITIES
Volume One in a Sunshine and Joy series

Published by

Sunshine and Joy Enterprises
P.O. Box 872
Bedford, TX 76095-0872

Copyright © 2007 Sunshine and Joy Enterprises

First printed in the United States of America, February 2007

ISBN-13: 978-0-9793634-0-5
ISBN-10: 0-9793634-0-3

Cover design by Cesar Hernandez.

For those with Alzheimer's disease and the loving people who commit their time and energy to caring for them. May a cure soon be found.

Sunshine & Joy

Adapted from "The Word"
by John Kendrick Bangs

Today, whatever may annoy,
The word for me is simply joy:
    The joy of life;
    The joy of children and of wife;
    The joy of sunshine and blue skies;
    The joy of rain; the glad surprise
    Of twinkling stars that shine at night;
    The joy of winged things upon their flight;
    The joy of noonday, and the tried
    True joyousness of eventide;
    The joy of labor, and of mirth;
    The joy of air, and sea, and earth - -
Whatever there be of sorrow
I'll put off until tomorrow,
    And when tomorrow comes, why then
    'Twill be today and joy again!

Table of Contents

Foreword by Joe B. Ventimiglia, M.D., Ph.D... 2

Preface.. 5

Acknowledgements... 7

Safety.. 8

Helpful Hints.. 9

Credits.. 125

Fill-in-the-Blank Activities

What the Optimist Said.. 21

What the Builder Said.. 46

What the Clockmaker Said.. 63

Things Dad Might Have Said... 83

Relationship Advice... 97

Soap Operas... 45

Under the Hood.. 58

Georgy Porgy.. 58

Anacrostic.. 76

Song Titles... 84

Fictional Pairs... 99

Recall Activities

Where Am I?... 24

Who... Who... Who?.. 40

Who Am I?.. 52

Make-a-Choice Activities

Did Somebody Say "Witch"?.. 34

Sweet Treats Catalog and Instructions...................................... 47

Comparing Apples to Oranges... 85

True or False?... 93

Say When!.. 95

Sunshine Strips

    Instructions... 108

    Strip 1: Things in an Office... 109

    Strip 2: Things in a Kitchen.. 111

Attracting Attention

Stickers... 81

Observation Activities (Let's Talk About the Picture)

The African Elephant.. 28

The Taj Mahal.. 64

Plymouth Lighthouse.. 86

Reminiscing Activities (All About Me)

Remembering My Best Friend.. 15

Thanksgiving Day.. 27

Let's Eat... 38

My Money Habits.. 43

Playing Cards.. 55

Remembering Mother... 67

My First Job.. 85

Open Wide.. 99

Matching Activity

Flash Card Instructions.. 107

Flash Cards... 113

Advice-Giving Activities

Frank's Office Advice - A Big Raise... 16

Gary's Green Thumb Advice - Aphids... 34

Rules of Etiquette - Party Manners.. 35

Walt's Auto Advice - Air Conditioner Problem............................. 51

Ruth's Advice About Children - Wild Neighbor Kids...................... 69

Ask Hazel - Picky Mother-in-Law.. 74

Maude's Financial Advice - How to Spend a Bonus........................ 90

Betty's Home Remedies - Snoring.. 97

Art Activities

Scrapbook

    Instructions... 18

    Scrapbook Page... 19

    Journal Page... 20

Heehaw.. 61

In the Garden.. 79

Fill-in-the-Drawing... 91

Greeting Cards

    Instructions... 102

    Card 1: Happy Birthday.. 103

    Card 2: How Are You?.. 105

Armchair Exercises

Let's Move.. 37

Question and Answer Activities

History

The Lindbergh Baby Kidnapping.. 26

Napoleon.. 44

The First Walk on the Moon.. 51

Fads and Fashions of the 1920's... 76

Cleopatra.. 90

American Presidents - Abraham Lincoln.. 98

Nature

Bird Calls.. 46

Under the Sea - Puffer Fish.. 59

Let's Talk About Ants.. 74

The Buzz About Beavers... 94

Travel

Road Trip - Michigan.. 17

Nashville, Tennessee.. 23

Let's Go Globetrotting - Canada.. 31

Road Trip - Kansas.. 32

Road Trip - Washington.. 39

Yellowstone National Park.. 42

Washington, D.C.. 45

Road Trip - Ohio... 57

Let's Go Globetrotting - Ireland.. 59

Road Trip - South Dakota... 75

Road Trip - Oregon.. 83

Let's Go Globetrotting - Greece.. 89

Let's Go Globetrotting - Madrid, Spain... 96

Entertainment

TV Trivia - *"I Love Lucy"*... 16

Now Starring Cary Grant.. 17

Movie Trivia - *"Gone With the Wind"*... 27

Movie Trivia - *"Citizen Kane"*... 40

Krazy Kartoons - *"Popeye"*... 41

Singers of Note - Trini Lopez.. 41

Music Menagerie... 44

Now Starring Grace Kelly... 50

TV Trivia - Game Shows... 53

Appearing Tonight: Roy Rogers... 60

Now Starring Fred Astaire and Ginger Rogers............................... 63

Movie Trivia - *"The Sound of Music"*... 68

Movie Trivia - *"Alice in Wonderland"*... 75

TV Trivia - *"The Little Rascals"*.. 94

Miscellaneous

Help Wanted: Waiter or Waitress.. 23

Time Magazine.. 24

On the Go - Hot Air Balloons.................................. 25

Calling All Cooks.. 26

Great Inventions - The Model T.............................. 54

Football Quiz.. 68

Help Wanted: School Bus Driver............................ 69

Signs of the Zodiac... 70

William Shakespeare... 77

How Does Your Garden Grow?.............................. 78

Food For Thought... 84

The Rainbow Quiz... 95

Game

Tic-Tac-Toe.. 56

Planning Activities

Let's Dine Out at a German Restaurant..................... 21

Let's Design Your Dream Job................................. 35

Let's Plan a Day Trip to Rome, Italy....................... 37

Let's Dine Out at a Chinese Restaurant.................... 53

Let's Plan a Day Trip to Melbourne, Australia............ 56

Let's Design Your Dream Kids............................... 93

Listening Activities

Mother Goose: *"Little Bo Peep"*........................... 22

Itty-Bitty Biography: John James Audubon................ 25

Amazing Facts... 32

Great Inventions: Barbie Doll, Jukebox, Washing Machine.......... 36

Famous Quotes.. 39

Classified Ads.. 42

Brush Up On Art: James McNeill Whistler................ 52

Lear's Limericks... 55

Famous Quotes.. 57

Classified Ads.. 72

Singing Activities

"Old MacDonald Had a Farm".............................. 33

"The Star-Spangled Banner"................................ 50

"The Farmer in the Dell"..................................... 73

Celebrate

Mark Your Calendar (Wacky but Real Dates to Celebrate)............ 100

Award Ribbons.. 117

Bonus Material for Caregivers

.... 119

FAVORITE THINGS

FAVORITE ACTIVITIES:	PAGE NUMBER:

FAVORITE TOPICS FOR CONVERSATION:

Foreword

Alzheimer's disease (AD) is a foe with an increasingly common and recognizable face in today's medical landscape. It is the most common disease that causes impairment of thinking and memory in the elderly, and is a major focus of healthcare, with annual expenditures for treatment exceeding $60 billion per year. Alzheimer's affects more than 4 million Americans annually, with famous sufferers such as former President Ronald Reagan bringing the disease into sharper public focus. With the historic shift of the median age of the American population reaching an all-time high within the next 5 – 10 years, and the fact that the incidence of AD doubles every five years after the age of 60, the number of sufferers and the economic and social burden imposed by this illness stands to make an even more pronounced impact.

Despite the specter that AD creates for geriatric healthcare now and in the future, there is no cure for the illness at this time. Sufferers (or PALs as more humanely and creatively dubbed in this book) and their families face an often long and excruciating course of decline in memory, mental function and behavior. PALs in the advanced phases of the disease often become completely unresponsive, bed bound, and unable to swallow food, drink, or to communicate. A number of "disease modifying" medications are currently available that help the parts of the brain most affected by AD. These medications maintain a more extended supply of the chemicals that help the nerve cells in this part of the brain to function somewhat better. Other medications can help to calm some of the disturbing agitation and hallucinations that can occur with advanced AD. None of these drugs, however, do more than slow the progression of the illness, leaving PALs and their families with a bit more quality time under the best of circumstances.

Caregivers of PALs can do many common-sense things to help improve the overall safety and quality of life of PALs, such as eliminate furnishings and circumstances that are physically dangerous. Medical practices can offer physician house calls and other home health services to help improve the logistics of care delivery. However, caregiver burnout and depression are common for PALs' families and caregivers since the medical community has offered few substantive interventions that make a real impact on the progress and quality of life for PALs. It is precisely at this point of need that I find *Sunshine and Joy's Big Book of Alzheimer's Activities* to be such an exciting, unique, and welcome contribution to the universe of care for AD.

I had the privilege of meeting Jill Hernandez and her PAL, Joan, in August of 2002, in my capacity as her house call primary care physician, and my house call group practice has continued to serve in the capacity of primary care provider for Joan since that time. Jill is always an inspiring caregiver to work with in caring for her PAL. Her initiative and refusal to give in to the frustrations facing caregivers of this disease, and her fiercely proactive posture in facing the AD in her family with courage, grace, and intelligence, is a model of how much of a difference that kind of commitment can make. Joan has always been one of the more radiant PALs that I've worked with. Her million dollar smile and trademark, red-sequined hats reflect the love, care, and meticulous attention she gets from Jill and the family. Jill's book, *Sunshine and Joy's Big Book of Alzheimer's Activities,* takes this contribution to the next level by sharing with the AD community a well-thought-out series of verbal and other structural activities to enhance the day to day cognitive work of the PAL. It does this in a manner that is socially engaging with the caregiver, interesting, contextually and historically relevant to PALs of the current generation of sufferers, rich in color, and just fun. But more than just offering an empty exercise, there is emerging evidence in the medical literature that socially rich, cognitively engaging puzzles like those lovingly offered in this book may actually forestall or prevent the dementia and cognitive decline that characterizes dementia.

We are still miles away from a cure, but I welcome Jill's book into my arsenal of materials that I will offer to AD families and their PALs to make life better in the meantime.

Joe B. Ventimiglia, M.D., Ph.D.
Family Practice * House Calls, P.A.
Las Colinas, Texas
February 2007

Our PALs

Throughout this book, I use the acronym "PAL" to mean a Person with ALzheimer's disease. A PAL may be a parent, grandparent, spouse, or friend. I also use the term "PALs" to refer collectively to people with Alzheimer's disease.

Preface

My father lovingly cared for my mother during the first years after she was diagnosed with Alzheimer's disease. When his own illness prevented him from caring for her any longer, he made the difficult decision to place her in a nursing home.

Two years later, my mother suffered a debilitating stroke. My husband and I decided to bring her home to live with us. I was confident I could manage her physical needs, but I felt overwhelmed by the task of stimulating her mind and amusing her during the long days at home. I began searching for books with activities appropriate for those with Alzheimer's disease. I was to be disappointed in the quest. I found many books with activity suggestions that sounded good on paper, but which failed when I attempted them with my mother.

To begin with, the books often contained activities unsuited to the abilities of a PAL.* Craft and recipe activities, for example, generally contain a sequence of steps. Following a sequence requires something PALs lack, namely, a good short-term memory. Even a simple "Cut out a square, then paste it here" can be confusing. In the nursing home, I watched many craft activities rapidly reach a "passive observer" stage where caregivers were doing the craft while PALs merely looked on.

Secondly, many of the books suggested activities which required effort on my part. As anyone who has done it knows, caregiving is exhausting work. Gathering up materials for an activity involves extra time, expense, possibly a trip to the store, and clean-up. I particularly remember one book which suggested I organize a treasure hunt for my mother. First I would have to gather up the "treasures" (and later I would have to put them all away again). The author of this book failed to recognize that every day with a PAL is already a treasure hunt of sorts. Searching for misplaced items such as glasses, keys, articles of clothing, etc. more than satisfies our primitive hunting and gathering instincts.

Thirdly, many books merely stated the obvious. One suggested putting on some music for my mother. Another recommended she make her bed every morning. I stifled a yawn as I waded through pages of suggestions to fold clothes, collect fallen leaves or seashells, watch television, go for a walk, bake a pie, etc. We had already "been there, done that." Quite frankly, we had long ago grown bored with chores and other ordinary activities of daily life. I needed a book with fun and stimulating activities to lift my mother <u>beyond</u> the routine.

* PAL = <u>P</u>erson with <u>AL</u>zheimer's

Lastly, there were books suggesting visits to a zoo, museum, or park. (At the latter place, "Go fly a kite" was the suggestion as well as my reaction.) Caregivers know that outings can be physically taxing for PALs. Moreover, feelings of disorientation and anxiety are often exacerbated by new surroundings.

Thus, with the shortage of material containing practical activities, a project was born. My goal was to develop activities that would truly engage and entertain a PAL, and could be done at home with little to no additional effort on the part of caregivers. My book is filled with conversational activities. Whether you have half an hour before dinner comes out of the oven, or several hours of idle time to fill on a rainy day, there are plenty of activities to challenge your PAL and entertain you both. When you leave home, the book becomes a portable resource. You can use it, for example, to while away the time in a doctor's office.

As a footnote, I'm happy to say my mother made a complete recovery from her stroke and we recently passed the four-year anniversary of her move "home." I'm convinced that keeping her mind active played a great role both in her recovery and in her continuing interest and participation in life. It is to her that I owe the inspiration for this book.

Jill Hernandez

Acknowledgements

Foremost, I would like to thank my mother, Joan, who has Alzheimer's disease and who, with great humor, allowed me to use her as a test subject for these activities. Her important contribution toward this work is one of the many reasons she is my hero.

I would like to thank my dear friend, Jaimee, who tirelessly researched much of the material for this book. Her energy and enthusiasm for the project spurred me on during times when the volume of work seemed overwhelming.

I would like to recognize Martin for his help with the content, Carmen for her heart-felt support, and Laura for her most valuable feedback.

Last, but by no means least, I would like to thank my husband, Cesar, who cheerfully and enthusiastically supported my efforts every step of the way. His outstanding talents as an artist are evident in the design of the book's cover, and he made many insightful contributions to the book's contents.

CAUTION!

SAFETY FIRST

A few activities in this book involve the use of pens, pencils, and blunt scissors. <u>Do not</u> leave your PAL alone and within reach of any item which could be a choking hazard or which could harm your PAL in any other way. Even paper can become a choking hazard. Don't take anything for granted. Always supervise the use of these items and be safe!

Helpful Hints

The order in which the hints are given does not indicate relative importance. Each PAL* is a unique individual, and what works for one may be of no use to another. With this in mind, please take a moment to read through <u>all</u> of the hints and adopt those which are most helpful to your PAL.

GET COMFORTABLE

Make sure your PAL is comfortably situated and relaxed. Eliminate distractions such as:

- Objects within reach. Your PAL may be tempted to fidget with them.

- Noise from a radio or television, or from other people talking nearby. Your PAL may be unable to isolate your voice from other sounds, hearing instead a jumbled stream of words. Focus your PAL's attention by ensuring that yours is the only voice they hear.

- Mirrors or large windows that might present confusing reflections.

MIRROR, MIRROR

You may have noticed that PALs are very astute observers of your expressions and attitudes. They will often mirror your emotions, matching your smile with one of their own, or punctuating your laughter with a chuckle. Likewise, your PAL may react negatively to signs of impatience or frustration. Your PAL depends on you for reassurance that all is well, so smile, smile, smile!

NO SCOREKEEPING

Create an atmosphere where there is no such thing as failure. The activities are meant to make you and your PAL feel good. If your PAL gives you a wrong answer, you can still say "Yes, that's right!" Your PAL was engaged and may have known the answer, but was unable to verbalize it correctly at that moment. Remember, the goal is participation and fun, not accuracy.

* PAL = <u>P</u>erson with <u>AL</u>zheimer's

ATTENTION GRABBERS

Try to get your PAL's full attention when doing an activity. Rather than sit side by side, face one another. Your PAL will be better able to focus on you and see the nonverbal cues in your gestures and expressions.

If your PAL's attention wanders, precede questions with your PAL's name. For example, "Jean, did you know that grasshoppers can leap ten times their length?"

If you're still having trouble, gently take your PAL's hand in your own and say something like:

- "I'd like to talk with you."
- "I have a question for you."
- "May I ask you something?"
- "I'll bet you know the answer to this."

A physical touch usually works wonders to refocus your PAL's attention on you.

SPRINGBOARDS TO CONVERSATION

Though you may be sorely tested, resist the impulse to reason with your PAL or to be drawn into an argument about the accuracy of something your PAL said. It's best to simply redirect your PAL's attention by moving on to the next question or the next topic. Treat the questions as springboards to further conversation, not tests.

ADJUST YOUR TEMPO

Be sure to give your PAL plenty of time to respond to your questions. It may take awhile for your PAL to form the answers. If ample time elapses with no response, repeat or rephrase the question, or move on.

BE FLEXIBLE

If the questions and answers digress into other topics, don't worry. It's a sign that your PAL is responding and interested! Just let the conversation flow naturally. You can always resume the rest of an activity later.

CLAMMING UP

If your PAL looks away when you ask a question, it might be a sign that the question is too difficult. Your PAL may be embarrassed at not knowing the answer and may be trying to spare you any disappointment.

Your PAL's ability to answer certain kinds of questions may vary from day to day, or even from hour to hour. Learn to read your PAL's mood and energy level, and feel free to change the difficulty level of the questions as needed. To illustrate how you can easily alter the difficulty level, let's start with the following question:

What does the word "aloha" mean?

This question requires total recall on the part of your PAL. If your PAL seems stumped, try rephrasing the question as:

Does the word "aloha" mean "I'm sorry" or "hello"?

This question presents a simple choice. Your PAL has a 50/50 chance of answering the question successfully. If your PAL is still puzzled, change the question to:

Does the word "aloha" mean hello?

This question is slightly easier because it requires only a "yes" or "no" answer. If your PAL is still unresponsive, rephrase it as a "did you know" question:

Did you know that the word "aloha" means hello?

"Yes" and "no" are both correct answers to this type of question. Even a nod or a shrug will do.

For some PALs, you may need to work backward from this scenario and make easy questions more difficult.

TAKE NOTES

As you are doing the activities in this book, take note of the topics and memories that are of particular delight to your PAL. Record them on the "My Favorites" page which appears after the Table of Contents. On days when your PAL needs an extra pick-me-up, jump right to your PAL's favorite topics.

ADJUST REDUNDANCY AS NEEDED

In some activities, the phrasing is deliberately redundant, particularly with respect to the use of nouns, including people's names.

Continually refreshing your PAL's memory about the subject matter is a kindness, particularly for those PALs who are having trouble with short-term memory.

Take this set of questions for example:

> Do penguins have webbed feet?
> Are <u>they</u> black and white?
> Can <u>they</u> fly?

In this book, these questions would become:

> Do penguins have webbed feet?
> Are <u>penguins</u> black and white?
> Can <u>penguins</u> fly?

MOVE ON

There may be times when the conversation just isn't flowing. It doesn't necessarily mean that your PAL is not thinking about the subject matter. It may just be that it's difficult to articulate an answer at that particular moment. Switch to a less demanding activity such as a song or a listening activity.

Now and again, you may inadvertently stumble across an unpleasant memory. If it's not the sort of memory that can be laughed about in retrospect, it's best not to probe but to move on quickly to the next question or an entirely new topic.

"ALL ABOUT ME" ACTIVITIES

Reminiscing is a wonderful way to connect with your PAL. It's always nice to revisit pleasant memories and the familiarity of the subject matter may be perceived by your PAL as a safe harbor. Because this activity is generally so successful, you will find a wide variety of interview material in the "All About Me" activities.

There are nearly 100 biographical topics contained within the entire series of Sunshine and Joy's Big Book of Alzheimer's activities. Taken together, the answers form quite a comprehensive life story.

"WHOA! I'M NOT RECITING NURSERY RHYMES!"

Most adults would never dream of reciting rhymes to anyone but a child.

Consider though, that while your PAL may be frustrated by the question "What did you have for breakfast this morning?" you can say "Row, row, row your ____" and be assured that most PALs will immediately chime in "BOAT!"

This is because nursery rhymes and childhood songs are familiar, something that many of us learn early in life and pass on to the next generation. For most people, these are pleasant memories and many PALs will listen to or recite nursery rhymes without embarrassment, indeed with pleasure because it's something they know and recognize.

Bottom line: Answering questions correctly gives your PAL a sense of accomplishment. Embrace those things that give your PAL a sense of accomplishment and evoke pleasant memories.

DRAW ATTENTION TO YOUR PAL

Next time you expect company or go on an outing with your PAL, place one of the "ice-breaker" stickers in a prominent spot on your PAL's shirt, blouse, or hat. (Stickers are provided in this book.) I think you'll be pleasantly surprised by the number of people who notice the sticker and go out of their way to speak a few kind words to your PAL. It makes everyone feel good.

KUDOS

Everyone likes a pat on the back now and then. This book offers many opportunities to praise your PAL for a job well done. Occasionally present your PAL with one of the award ribbons we've included in this book. Doing so is a nice way to let them know that you appreciate them and, like the stickers, it draws the attention of others to your PAL in a positive way.

WATCH FOR FATIGUE

If you repeatedly have to refocus your PAL with attention grabbers, it may be a sign of fatigue. Never feel you have to finish an activity once you've started. The book is meant to be picked up and put down on the spur of the moment.

NOW…let's get started!

All About Me

Remembering My Best Friend

1. Tell me the name of your best friend in high school.
2. Were you and (insert name) the same age?
3. What did (name) look like?
4. Do you remember how you met (name)?
5. What did you like most about (name)?
6. Did (name) ever do anything to make you mad?
7. Did you have any classes with (name)? What were they?
8. Did you spend a lot of time with (name) after school? What did you do together?
9. Did you and (name) study together?
10. Was (name) a good student?
11. Did (name) live nearby?
12. Did you ever stay overnight at (name)'s house? Was it fun?
13. Did (name) have brothers and sisters you played with?
14. Did you tell (name) all your secrets? Did (name) keep your secrets?
15. Did you and (name) ever have a crush on the same girl/boy?
16. Did (name) ever fix you up with a blind date?
17. Did you and (name) ever get into trouble? What did you do?
18. Did you and (name) dress alike? Did you borrow each other's clothes?
19. Did you and (name) spend a lot of time talking on the telephone?
20. Did you and (name) have a favorite place to "hang out" together?
21. Did you keep in touch with (name) after high school?

Dear Frank,

One of my co-workers, Earl, just got a big raise. I think he gets special treatment because he's married to the boss's daughter. I work a lot harder than Earl does and I think I deserve a raise too. What should I do?

Sincerely, Ray

Frank's Office Advice

What do **YOU** think Ray should do?

A. Should Ray say to his boss, "You'd better give me a raise too, or I'm quitting"?
B. Should Ray have a heart-to-heart talk with his boss and tell him why he thinks he deserves a raise also?
C. Should Ray tell his boss that Earl is lazy, and that it was a mistake to give him a raise?
D. Should Ray quit his job because he didn't get a raise?

"I Love Lucy"

Trivia

1. In the 1950's, one of the most popular TV shows was *"I Love _ _ _ _ (Lucy)."*
2. *"I Love Lucy"* starred Desi Arnaz and Lucille _ _ _ _ (Ball).
3. Lucy's husband is a bandleader named Ricky _ _ _ _ _ _ _ (Ricardo).
4. Lucy and Ricky's best friends are Fred and Ethel _ _ _ _ _ (Mertz).
5. When Ricky gets mad, does he yell in French or in Spanish? (Spanish)
6. What color is Lucy Ricardo's hair? (Red)
7. Did Lucy and Ethel once steal John Wayne's footprints? (Yes)
8. Lucy and Ricky's son is nicknamed Little _ _ _ _ _ (Ricky).
9. Lucy Ricardo is always trying to get into show _ _ _ _ _ _ _ _ (business).
10. Did Lucy once get drunk on Vitameatavegamin? (Yes)

… Can you say Vitameatavegamin quickly, three times?

Road Trip

MICHIGAN
3 Miles ⟹

1. Did you know the name "Michigan" comes from a Chippewa Indian word meaning "great water"?
2. The first aviator to fly solo across the Atlantic Ocean was from Michigan. His name was Charles Lind_ _ _ _ _ (bergh).
3. Did you know that singer Diana Ross grew up in Michigan?
4. Did you know that Michigan has more recreational boats than any other state?
5. Detroit, Michigan is known as the Car Capital of the _ _ _ _ _ (World).
6. Did you know that Michigan has more shoreline than any other state except Alaska?
7. Michigan has an official state game animal. Is it the white-tailed rabbit or the white-tailed deer? (White-tailed deer).
8. Did you know that one of the largest herds of moose in the United States lives on Isle Royale in Michigan?

Now Starring Cary Grant

1. Did you know that Cary Grant was born in England?
2. In 1938, Cary Grant starred with Katherine Hepburn in a comedy called *"Bringing Up _ _ _ _ (Baby)."*
3. Was "Baby" a pet monkey or a pet leopard? (Leopard)
4. Is it true that Cary Grant became an American citizen in 1942? (Yes)
5. In 1948, Cary Grant had a role in a movie called *"Mr. Blandings Builds His Dream _ _ _ _ _ (House)."*
6. Did Cary Grant ever win an Oscar for Best Actor? (No)
7. Is it true that in 1944, Cary Grant gave his $100,000 salary for his role in *"Arsenic and Old Lace"* to the U.S. war effort? (Yes)
8. Cary Grant played the part of a doctor in a comedy called *"Every Girl Should be _ _ _ _ _ _ _ (Married)."*
9. In a movie called *"That Touch of Mink,"* Cary Grant is a rich businessman who is attracted to an old-fashioned country girl played by Doris _ _ _ (Day).
10. Would you say that Cary Grant was a handsome, well-dressed man?

Scrapbook Page

A scrapbook can be a wonderful resource on days when it's difficult to engage your PAL in other types of activities. Looking at photographs and talking and laughing about good memories may capture your PAL's interest and guide his or her thoughts into pleasant channels.

A scrapbook can also be a great resource for others who spend time with your PAL. It can help them get acquainted and give them something to talk about.

Attach a photograph or memento to the blank space on the following scrapbook page. Space is provided on the back of the scrapbook page for you to record special memories.

You may leave the scrapbook page intact with this activity book or remove it and include it in a separate scrapbook. Answers to the "All About Me" questions, completed artwork pages, and ribbon awards are a few of the many activities that would make great accompaniments to your favorite photographs.

Ask your PAL for input as you create the page(s). Ask your PAL which photos you should use and where you should paste them. Talk out loud as you're deciding what to write in the journal spaces. If something you say prompts a laugh or a smile now, there's a good chance you'll get the same response when you next sit down together to look at the scrapbook.

A memory that made
us smile or laugh:

A
FUNNY THING
THAT
HAPPENED:

Make new friends,
But keep the old,
One is silver,
And the other gold!

Something fun we did together:

Why you're special:

LET'S DINE OUT

"The German Restaurant"

1. At the German restaurant, would you like to try a glass of German beer before the meal?
2. Would you like a cup of linsensuppe (lentil soup) or kartoffelsuppe (potato soup)?
3. With the soup, would you like pumpernickel bread or just a plain roll?
4. Would you like some bratwurst (German sausage)?
5. Would you like to try schweinebraten (roast pork)?
6. Would you like a side order of sauerkraut (pickled cabbage)?
7. Would you like some German potato dumplings with your meal?
8. For dessert, would you like a slice of Black Forest cake?
9. Would you like to try some strong German coffee with dessert?
10. Would you like to order some lebkuchen (gingerbread) to take home?

Fill in the *BLANK*

What the OPTIMIST said…

1. Keep your chin _ _ (up).
2. Don't worry, be _ _ _ _ _ (happy)!
3. Hope springs _ _ _ _ _ _ _ _ (eternal).
4. Never say _ _ _ _ _ (never).
5. When my ship comes _ _ (in).
6. Eat, drink, and be _ _ _ _ _ (merry).
7. I'm happy-go-_ _ _ _ _ (lucky).
8. There's a pot of gold at the end of the _ _ _ _ _ _ _ (rainbow).
9. While there's life, there's _ _ _ _ (hope).
10. Don't make a mountain out of a _ _ _ _ _ _ _ _ (molehill).

Do You Remember...

LITTLE BO-PEEP

Little Bo-Peep has lost her _ _ _ _ _ (sheep),
And can't tell where to find them;
Leave them alone, and they'll come _ _ _ _ (home),
Bringing their tails behind them.

Little Bo-Peep fell fast asleep,
And dreamt she heard them bleating;
But when she awoke, she found it a joke,
For still they all were fleeting.

Then up she took her little crook,
Determined for to find them;
She found them indeed, but it made her heart bleed,
For they'd left all their tails behind 'em!

It happened one day, as Bo-Peep did stray
Unto a meadow hard by--
There she espied their tails, side by side,
All hung on a tree to dry.

She heaved a sigh and wiped her eye,
And over the hillocks she raced;
And tried what she could, as a shepherdess should,
That each tail should be properly placed.

Nashville

1. Is Nashville the capital of Tennessee? (Yes)
2. Is Nashville known as the home of rock music or country music? (Country music)
3. Did the Grand Ole Opry radio show begin in Nashville in 1925 or 1955? (1925)
4. Is Nashville often referred to as the "Athens of the South" because of its many classical style buildings? (Yes)
5. Is Nashville's football team known as the Tennessee Giants or the Tennessee Titans? (Tennessee Titans)
6. If you live in Nashville, would you be called a Nashvillite or a Nashvillian? (Nashvillian)
7. Did you know that the first FM radio station began in Nashville in 1947?
8. Have you ever been to Nashville? Did you enjoy your visit?

Wanted: Waiter or Waitress

1. Would you like to apply for a job as a waiter or waitress?
2. Have you had any previous experience working in a restaurant? Tell me about it.
3. Do you enjoy working with the public?
4. Would you mind wearing a uniform while on the job?
5. As a waiter or waitress, would you mind being on your feet all day?
6. Would you be good at memorizing and reciting the daily lunch specials?
7. What would you say to a customer who couldn't make up his mind about what to order?
8. If there were 8 people at a table, would you be able to keep all of their orders straight?
9. How many platters of food can you carry at one time?
10. What would you say to a customer who complained that the soup was cold?
11. If a customer forgot his wallet, would you make him wash dishes to pay for his meal?
12. Would you share your tips with the busboys and busgirls?

Where Am I?

1. I'm on a ride called "Pirates of the Caribbean." Where am I? (Disneyland)
2. I'm driving across the Golden Gate Bridge. Where am I? (San Francisco, California)
3. I'm looking up at Big Ben. Where am I? (London, England)
4. I'm standing on the ice and I've just spotted a polar bear in the distance. Where am I? (In the arctic)
5. I've just reached the top of the highest mountain in the world. Where am I? (Mount Everest)
6. I've just left the Flamingo Hotel and I'm headed for Caesar's Palace. Where am I? (Las Vegas, Nevada)
7. I just left the OK Corral and I'm on my way to the Crystal Palace Saloon. Where am I? (Tombstone, Arizona)
8. I see a whole lot of bats hanging overhead. And it's so dark in here! Where am I? (In a cave)

Time Magazine

1. Do you ever read *Time* magazine?
2. Does *Time* magazine's cover have a bright red border? (Yes)
3. Is it true that you can read political news and other current events in *Time* magazine? (Yes)
4. Did you know that *Time* magazine has editions published in Europe, Asia, Canada, and the South Pacific?
5. Is *Time* magazine published every month or every week? (Every week)
6. Is it true that Adolf Hitler was once *Time* magazine's "Man of the Year"? (Yes)
7. Has Marilyn Monroe ever been on the cover of *Time* magazine? (Yes, twice.)
8. Has Abraham Lincoln ever been on the cover of *Time* magazine"? (Yes, three times.)
9. Was the first *Time* magazine created in 1923 or 1953? (1923)
10. Did you know that Richard Nixon holds the record for being on the most *Time* magazine covers?

An Itty-Bitty Biography
of
John James Audubon

~ John James Audubon was born in 1785. He grew up in France.

~ From an early age, Audubon was fond of sketching birds.

~ When Audubon was 18, his father sent him to America to avoid being drafted into Napoleon's army.

~ Audubon began as a true "starving artist." At the age of 34, he went to jail for bankruptcy.

~ Audubon went on to paint all of the birds in North America, a grand project.

~ Audubon had the paintings engraved and bound into very large books.

~ Each book had 435 engravings. Since color printing hadn't been invented yet, each of the large engravings had to be colored by hand.

~ Audubon's books are widely regarded as the finest picture books ever made.

~ In the 1830's, Audubon was able to sell his books for about $1,000 apiece.

~ One of Audubon's books was recently sold for about $9 million dollars.

~ John James Audubon is buried in Manhattan, New York.

ON the GO

"Hot Air Balloons"

1. Are hot air balloons often very colorful? (Yes)
2. Do hot air balloon passengers ride in a buggy or a basket? (Basket)
3. Did you know that some hot air balloons can carry up to 12 passengers?
4. In a hot air balloon, would you have a good, bird's-eye view of the ground below? (Yes)
5. Are hot air balloons usually flown at night or early in the morning? (Early in the morning, when winds are most favorable.)
6. Is a hot air balloon's direction determined by steering or wind? (Wind)
7. Did you know that when you're in a hot air balloon, you don't feel any wind? You don't feel the wind because you're moving along with it.
8. Is it true you need a pilot's license to carry passengers in a hot air balloon? (Yes)
9. A man from India took a hot air balloon more than 13 miles high! Would you like to go 13 miles high in a hot air balloon?
10. Have you ever ridden in a hot air balloon? Tell me about it.

Calling All Cooks

1. How many drumsticks are there on a turkey? (Two)
2. Is chili usually spicy? (Yes)
3. Does pumpkin pie contain sugar? (Yes)
4. Is a rolling pin used when making a pie crust? (Yes)
5. Would cinnamon be a good seasoning for an apple pie? (Yes)
6. Is sour cream an ingredient you might find in dip? (Yes)
7. Which would taste better with turkey: cranberry sauce or chocolate sauce? (Cranberry sauce)
8. Which is a main ingredient of succotash: pumpkin or lima beans? (Lima beans)
9. If the recipe calls for poaching an egg, are they asking you to steal one? (No, they mean for you to cook it in water.)
10. To make deviled eggs, must you start with hard-boiled eggs? (Yes)

The Lindbergh Baby Kidnapping

1. Did you know that in 1927, Charles Lindbergh became the first pilot to fly solo over the Atlantic Ocean?
2. Charles Lindbergh's baby was kidnapped. Was the baby a little boy or a little girl? (Boy)
3. Was the Lindbergh baby kidnapped in 1932 or 1952? (1932)
4. Was the baby kidnapped from the Lindbergh's home? (Yes)
5. Did the baby's kidnapper leave a ransom note demanding money? (Yes)
6. Was the kidnapper of the Lindbergh baby caught and brought to justice? (Yes)

MOVIE TRIVIA
"Gone With the Wind"

1. A famous American Civil War epic is *"Gone with the _ _ _ _ (Wind)."*
2. *"Gone with the Wind"* starred Vivien Leigh and Clark _ _ _ _ _ _ (Gable).
3. A main character in *"Gone with the Wind"* is Scarlett _' _ _ _ _ (O'Hara).
4. Scarlett O'Hara lives on a cotton plantation. Is it called Twelve Oaks or Tara? (Tara)
5. Scarlett often says "Fiddle-dee-_ _ _ (dee)."
6. When Scarlett has no money for a new dress, does she have one made from Tara's green velvet curtains? (Yes)
7. Rhett Butler gets fed up with Scarlett and tells her, "Frankly, my dear, I don't give a _ _ _ _ (damn)."
8. Scarlett's last line in *"Gone with the Wind"* is "After all, tomorrow is another _ _ _ (day)."

   ... Do you think Rhett Butler should have given Scarlett another chance?

All About Me
Thanksgiving Day

1. When you were a kid, did your mother prepare a big turkey for Thanksgiving Day?
2. Have you ever cooked a big Thanksgiving Day dinner?
3. Do you get together with relatives on Thanksgiving Day?
4. Do you like to watch the Macy's Thanksgiving Day Parade on TV? Have you ever been to see it in person?
5. What time should Thanksgiving dinner be served?
6. Have you ever carved a turkey? Does it take any skill? How do you go about carving a turkey?
7. Do you like to pull the wishbone? What kind of wish would you make if you had a wishbone now?
8. Do you always eat too much on Thanksgiving Day? Do you end up with a lot of leftover food on Thanksgiving? What do you do with the leftovers?

Let's Talk About the Picture

"African Elephants"

Show the picture to your PAL while asking these questions:

1. What animal is shown in this picture? (Elephant)
2. Elephants are vegetarians. They like to eat bark, leaves, fruit, and grass. Is there grass near the elephant in this picture? (Yes)
3. How many tusks does this elephant have? (Two)
4. Is this elephant wrinkled? (Yes)
5. Is this elephant an adult or a baby? (Adult)
6. Does this elephant have its trunk up in the air? (No)

Did you know...

1. African elephants can weigh as much as 13,000 pounds. An African elephant eats 16 hours a day. A baby African elephant can weigh as much as 250 pounds.
2. Elephants have very poor vision.
3. African elephants have large ears, long ivory tusks, and a strong trunk.
4. The African elephant flaps its large ears to keep cool and to keep bugs away.
5. African elephants roll in dust and mud to protect their sensitive skin from sunburn. It also protects them from insect bites.
6. African elephants live to be about 70 years old.

29

Let's Go Globetrotting!

Canada

1. Is Canada the largest or second largest country in the world? (Second largest)

2. Did early explorers go to Canada in search of prairie dogs or beavers? (Beavers)

3. Is Canada part of North America or South America? (North America)

4. Canada has a long border with the United States. Does it border any other country? (No)

5. Is part of Niagara Falls located in Canada? (Yes)

6. Is the Queen of England also the Queen of Canada? (Yes)

7. Are there ten or twenty provinces in Canada? (Ten)

8. Is Canada's capital Ottawa or Ontario? (Ottawa)

9. Is Nova Scotia a part of Canada? (Yes)

10. What is pictured on the Canadian quarter: a caribou or a kangaroo? (Caribou)

11. A loon is featured on the Canadian dollar. Is a loon a bird or a fish? (Bird)

12. Does Canada have a president or a prime minister? (Prime minister)

13. Is the leaf on the Canadian flag a maple leaf or a fig leaf? (Maple leaf)

14. Have you ever visited Canada? Do you know anyone who lives in Canada?

Amazing Facts!

1. Did you know a tornado blew through Wichita Falls, Texas in 1958 at a speed of 280 miles per hour?
2. How would you like to catch a 660 pound catfish? The Mekong River in China is home to one of the biggest freshwater fish in the world, the giant catfish.
3. Did you know that 90% of the ice on earth is in Antarctica?
4. Did you know that Count Dracula has been in more movies than Frankenstein? Count Dracula appears in at least 162 films.
5. Did you know that the highest mountain in the solar system is over 16 miles high? The mountain is called Olympus Mons and it's located on Mars.
6. Have you ever been to the Woolly Worm Festival in Banner Elk, North Carolina? Over 20,000 people attend the festival to watch worms race up a three-foot length of string.

Road Trip

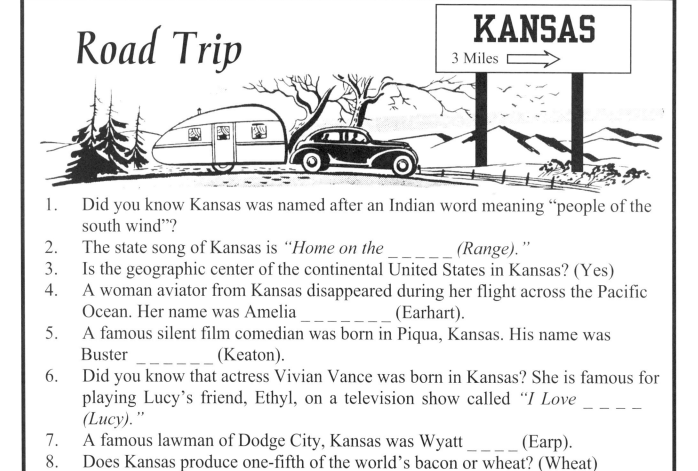

KANSAS
3 Miles

1. Did you know Kansas was named after an Indian word meaning "people of the south wind"?
2. The state song of Kansas is *"Home on the _ _ _ _ _ (Range)."*
3. Is the geographic center of the continental United States in Kansas? (Yes)
4. A woman aviator from Kansas disappeared during her flight across the Pacific Ocean. Her name was Amelia _ _ _ _ _ _ _ (Earhart).
5. A famous silent film comedian was born in Piqua, Kansas. His name was Buster _ _ _ _ _ _ (Keaton).
6. Did you know that actress Vivian Vance was born in Kansas? She is famous for playing Lucy's friend, Ethyl, on a television show called *"I Love _ _ _ _ (Lucy)."*
7. A famous lawman of Dodge City, Kansas was Wyatt _ _ _ _ (Earp).
8. Does Kansas produce one-fifth of the world's bacon or wheat? (Wheat)

Sing Along

"Old MacDonald Had a Farm"

Old MacDonald had a farm,
E-I-E-I-O,
And on his farm he had a cow,
E-I-E-I-O,
With a moo-moo here,
And a moo-moo there,
Here a moo, there a moo,
Everywhere a moo-moo.
Old MacDonald had a farm,
E-I-E-I-O.

Old MacDonald had a farm,
E-I-E-I-O,
And on his farm he had a pig,
E-I-E-I-O,
With an oink-oink here,
And an oink-oink there,
Here an oink, there an oink,
Everywhere an oink-oink.
Old MacDonald had a farm,
E-I-E-I-O.

Old MacDonald had a farm,
E-I-E-I-O,
And on his farm he had a duck,
E-I-E-I-O,
With a quack-quack here,
And a quack-quack there,
Here a quack, there a quack,
Everywhere a quack-quack..
Old MacDonald had a farm,
E-I-E-I-O.

Old MacDonald had a farm,
E-I-E-I-O,
And on his farm he had a donkey,
E-I-E-I-O,
With a hee-haw here,
And a hee-haw there,
Here a hee, there a haw,
Everywhere a hee-haw.
Old MacDonald had a farm,
E-I-E-I-O.

Did Somebody say "Witch"?

1. Which is damper: a swamp or a desert?
2. Which is curvier: a box or a beach ball?
3. Which is longer: a sprint or a marathon race?
4. Which is cuddlier: a toad or a teddy bear?
5. Which is softer: a poodle or a porcupine?
6. Which is more adorable: a kitten or an old pair of tennis shoes?
7. Which is more exclusive: a country club or a public library?
8. Which is more cheerful: a singing canary or a snoring gorilla?
9. Which is more dazzling: a diamond bracelet or a felt hat?
10. Which is more delicious: a milkshake or a tablespoon of cod liver oil?
11. Which is more fun: a visit to the dentist or a visit to the ice cream parlor?
12. Which is more efficient: taking the scenic route or going straight to your destination?

Dear Green Thumb Gary,

     HELP! My rosebushes are covered with aphids! What should I do?

     Sincerely, Maggie

Gary's Green Thumb Advice

What do **YOU** think Maggie should do?

A. Since aphids live only a short time, should Maggie just ignore them?
B. Should Maggie wash off the aphids with a strong spray of water?
C. Ladybugs love to eat aphids. Do you think Maggie should scatter ladybugs in her rosebushes?
D. A praying mantis will also eat aphids. Should Maggie put some praying mantises in her rosebushes also?
E. Garlic is a natural insect repellant. Should Maggie plant some garlic around her roses?
F. Should Maggie try a homemade remedy such as spraying her plants with soapy water to kill the aphids?

Rules of Etiquette
"Party Manners"

1. If somebody you know is throwing a party, is it okay to show up without an invitation?
2. Is it polite to arrive early at a party?
3. Would you take an uninvited guest with you to a party?
4. Is it okay to get drunk at a party? Is it okay to fall asleep on the sofa at a party?
5. Should you take a gift when you are invited to a birthday party?
6. Is it polite to say you're going to a party and then back out at the last minute?
7. Is it polite to ask the host or hostess if you can help clean up?
8. When you leave a party, should you thank the host and hostess and tell them what a great time you had?

...How do you know when it's time to leave a party?

 **Let's Design Your...**  **Dream Job!**

1. If you could have any job you wanted, would you like to work indoors or outdoors?
2. Would you rather work a day shift, a swing shift, or a graveyard shift?
3. If you could name your own salary, how much would you be making per year?
4. Would you like to be able to work from home?
5. Do you like to work with people or would you rather work alone?
6. Would you like to be self-employed or do you prefer to work for someone else?
7. Would you like to do a lot of traveling as part of your job?
8. Would you like to be able to take extra long breaks and lunches?
9. How many weeks of vacation would you have if it were up to you?
10. Would you like to work for an employer that provides you with a company car?

Great Inventions

The Barbie doll was invented by Ruth Handler in 1959. Barbie was named after Ruth's own daughter, Barbara. Most people don't know that Barbie's full name is Barbara Millicent Roberts. Her boyfriend's name is Ken and her first pet was a horse named Dancer. She has five sisters: Skipper, Tutti, Stacie, Kelly, and Krissy. The first Barbie sold for $3.00. In mint condition, an original 1959 Barbie doll has sold for as much as $10,000! Two Barbie dolls are sold every second!

The first Jukebox was made by the Automatic Music Instrument Company in 1927. Jukeboxes were named after the juke joints of the southern states. A juke joint was a place where field hands gathered for dancing. Jukebox production was halted during WWII to conserve labor and materials needed for the war effort. In 1946, the most popular model was made by Wurlitzer under the slogan "Wurlitzer IS Jukebox."

The earliest washing device was the scrub board invented in 1797. In 1874, an Indiana merchant, William Blackstone, built a birthday present for his wife. It was a wooden tub with a gear mechanism that swished clothes around in hot, soapy water. In about 1900, the wooden tub was replaced by a metal one. In 1908, the first electric washing machine arrived on the scene. Many early washing machines cost less than $10.

Let's Move!

1. Throw and catch a lightweight ball.
2. Can you bat your eyelashes?
3. With your arms at your sides, make a fist with your right hand. Bend your right elbow and bring your hand toward your right shoulder. Repeat with the left arm.
4. Pull imaginary weeds.
5. Tap your feet.
6. Can you teach me how to hula dance?
7. Shake maracas.

Let's Plan a Day Trip to Rome, ITALY

In Rome, we could start with a typical Italian breakfast of coffee and a small sweet roll called a cornetti. Does that sound good to you?

After breakfast, we could go to see the ancient Roman Coliseum. Do you enjoy looking at old ruins? Do you think anyone in Rome ever wears a toga these days?

Have you heard the expression, "When in Rome, do as the Romans do"? Would you like to stop for a cup of espresso around midday? It's what the Romans do!

Would you like to see the famous ceiling that Michelangelo painted in the Sistine Chapel? Sometimes you have to wait in line a long time to get in!

I think we should stop at the Trevi Fountain too. They say if you throw a coin into the fountain, it means you will return to Rome some day. Would you like to toss a coin into the fountain?

All About Me

Let's Eat

1. When you go out to eat, would you rather have fast food or dine in an expensive restaurant?
2. What is your favorite restaurant? Why is it your favorite?
3. If a restaurant parking lot is full, does it mean the food is good?
4. Do you like Chinese food? Can you eat with chopsticks? Do you look forward to getting a fortune cookie at the end of a meal?
5. Do you like pizza? What are your favorite pizza toppings?
6. Do you like Italian food? Which tastes better, lasagna or spaghetti? Do you like to roll spaghetti noodles on your fork or do you like to slurp them?
7. Are you a vegetarian?
8. Do you like Greek food? Did you ever break any plates after a Greek meal?
9. Do you like to eat bratwurst and sauerkraut?
10. Do you like salads? Do you think green salads are just "rabbit food"?
11. Do you like hamburgers and French fries?
12. Do you like your hamburgers plain or with "the works"?
13. Do you like Mexican food? Do you like hot sauce?
14. Have you ever been to a Japanese restaurant? Did you have to take your shoes off and sit on the floor?
15. Do you like to go to a good steak house? How do you like your steak: well done, medium, or rare?
16. Do you like seafood? Do you like lobster and crab?
17. Do you like to eat at the deli? What do you order there?
18. Do you like going out for ice cream or a snow cone?
19. Have you ever eaten so much at a restaurant that you had to undo a button or loosen your belt?

Road Trip

1. Did you know that Washington was named after George Washington?
2. Is Washington the only state named after a United States president? (Yes)
3. Does Washington have a volcano called Mount St. Helens? (Yes. It erupted in 1980.)
4. Two explorers arrived in Washington in 1805. Their names were Lewis and _ _ _ _ _ (Clark).
5. Washington's state gem is petrified _ _ _ _ (wood).
6. Game show host Bob Barker was born in Washington. He is famous for hosting a show called *"The Price is _ _ _ _ _ (Right)."*
7. Did you know that the largest dam in the United States is in Washington? It's called the Grand Coulee Dam.
8. Does Washington produce more apples than any other state? (Yes)

Famous Quotes

After one look at this planet, any visitor from outer space would say "I want to see the manager." --William Burroughs

Housework can't kill you, but why take a chance? -- Phyllis Diller

A vacation is what you take when you can no longer take what you've been taking. -- Earl Wilson

I grew up with six brothers. That's how I learned to dance - waiting for the bathroom. -- Bob Hope

MOVIE TRIVIA

"CITIZEN KANE"

1. Charles Foster Kane is a wealthy newspaper publisher in a movie titled *"Citizen _ _ _ _ (Kane)."*
2. *"Citizen Kane"* was rumored to be based in part on the life of real-life publishing tycoon William Randolph _ _ _ _ _ _ (Hearst).
3. Charles Foster Kane was played by Orson _ _ _ _ _ _ (Welles).
4. Kane's estate is named Xanadu. Is it in California or Florida? (Florida)
5. Kane says, "The news goes on for 24 hours a _ _ _ (day)."
6. In the movie *"Citizen Kane,"* Charles Foster Kane runs for political office. Does he run for the office of mayor or governor? (Governor)
7. Kane whispers a word just before he dies. Does he whisper "Carnation" or "Rosebud"? (Rosebud)
8. Is "Rosebud" a woman or a sled? (Sled)

…Charles Foster Kane collected statues. What do you collect?

Who... Who... Who?

1. Who followed the yellow brick road? (Dorothy)
2. Who is known as "The King of Rock and Roll"? (Elvis Presley)
3. Who has a glass slipper and is waiting for Prince Charming? (Cinderella)
4. Who has cute dimples and curls, and sang about the Good Ship Lollipop? (Shirley Temple)
5. Who was the first man to walk on the moon? (Neil Armstrong)
6. Who is Snoopy's best friend? (Charlie Brown)
7. Who is Superman when he's off-duty? (Clark Kent)
8. Who said "Lucy, I'm home"? (Ricky Ricardo)
9. Who hosted "The Tonight Show"? (Johnny Carson)
10. Who was the big band leader who played the clarinet and was known as the "King of Swing"? (Benny Goodman)

KRAZY KARTOONS
"Popeye"

1. Do you remember a cartoon called *"Popeye"*?
2. Is Popeye a fireman or a sailor? (Sailor)
3. Popeye's girlfriend is Olive _ _ _ (Oyl).
4. Does Popeye the Sailor have an anchor tattooed on his arm? (Yes)
5. Popeye has a friend named J. Wellington Wimpy. Does Wimpy love hotdogs or hamburgers? (Hamburgers)
6. Is the baby in *"Popeye"* called Willie or Swee'Pea? (Swee'Pea)
7. Does Popeye ever have to fight a big, bearded man called Bluto? (Yes)
8. When Popeye needs extra strength, does he open a can of peas or a can of spinach? (Spinach)
9. Did you know that Popeye has four nephews called Pip-Eye, Pup-Eye, Poop-Eye, and Peep-Eye?
10. Did you ever belong to the Popeye Club? Did you have a Popeye kazoo?

Singers of Note

1. Do you remember a singer named Trini Lopez? He was born in Dallas, Texas.
2. When Trini Lopez sang, did he play a piano or a guitar? (Guitar)
3. Trini Lopez was in a movie with Lee Marvin titled *"The Dirty _ _ _ _ _ (Dozen)."*
4. Did Trini Lopez have a hit song titled *"If I Had a Hammer"*? (Yes)
5. Trini Lopez sang a song about a lemon tree. He said the lemon flower is sweet but the fruit is impossible to _ _ _ (eat)!

Do you remember these songs sung by Trini Lopez:

"Bill Bailey, Won't You Please Come _ _ _ _ (Home)"
"Michael, Row the Boat A_ _ _ _ _ (shore)"
"I Love Your Beautiful Brown _ _ _ _ (Eyes)"
"That's What Makes the World Go '_ _ _ _ _ ('Round)"
"When the Saints Go Marching _ _ (In)"

Yellowstone National Park

1. Is it true that Yellowstone National Park is the first and oldest national park? (Yes)
2. Was Yellowstone National Park established in 1872 or 1972? (1872)
3. Are there any bald eagles living in Yellowstone National Park? (Yes)
4. Is Yellowstone National Park situated mainly in Wyoming or Montana? (Wyoming)
5. At Yellowstone National Park, would you be more likely to see grizzly bears or polar bears? (Grizzly bears)
6. Does Yellowstone National Park have more pine trees or aspen trees? (Pine trees)
7. Is it true that Yellowstone National Park has caves? (Yes)
8. One of the feature attractions of Yellowstone National Park is a geyser called "Old _ _ _ _ _ _ _ _(Faithful)."

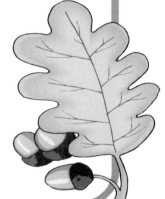

Classifieds

Circle the ads you're interested in.

Do you love champagne and roses? Single male, 72, seeks woman to enjoy life with. Call Melvin.

Piano lessons, all ages, all levels, beginners through advanced, your home or mine, $10/hr. Call Charlene.

For sale: Walnut desk, 3 drawers, 8 cubbyholes for papers. Comes with matching upholstered chair. $250 or best offer. Call Judy, evenings.

Experienced auto mechanic! All makes and models. Honest with good references. Reasonable rates. Call and ask for Mark.

Wanted: Ace Bank is seeking a qualified person for the position of teller. Apply in person and ask for Cornelius. Bring resume.

For Sale: Complete patio set – swing, 2 lounge chairs and one table. White wrought iron. Well cared for and in great condition! $75 for the set. Call Maria.

ABC Tools & Hardware is GOING OUT OF BUSINESS! Owner is retiring! 75% off everything in the store! Hurry in for best deals. Corner of 5th and Vine.

Now Accepting Applications! Manager position for Adela's Clothing Store. Previous sales experience required. Salary is negotiable. Call the store and ask for Roberta.

All About Me

My Money Habits

1. Did you get an allowance as a child? Did you save it or spend it?
2. Did you ever keep coins in a piggy bank? Did you ever have to break into your piggy bank? Why?
3. Do you believe in saving for a rainy day?
4. Are you a big spender?
5. When it comes to money, is it "easy come, easy go"?
6. Are you a big tipper?
7. Do you know anyone who's tight with a dollar?
8. Do you have a nest egg? Do you plan to spend your nest egg some day?
9. When you put bills in your wallet, do you sort them in order?
10. Do you like to carry a credit card?
11. Have you ever hidden money under the mattress or somewhere else? Did you ever forget where you hid it?
12. Did you ever lose your wallet or purse? How did that happen? Did you get it back?
13. Do you shop at the five and dime? What do you buy there?
14. Is it good luck to find a penny?
15. When you buy something, do you always save your receipt?
16. Did you ever forget to record a check in your checkbook?
17. Did you ever get to the checkout counter and realize you'd forgotten your wallet or your checkbook? What did you do?
18. Do you like to clip coupons? Did you ever save green stamps? What things could you buy with green stamps?
19. Do you like to buy things on sale?
20. Do you like to buy lottery tickets? Do you play the same numbers every time? Did you ever win the lottery?

Music Menagerie

Did you know that Ringo Starr's original name was Richard Starkey?

Did you ever hear a song called, *"When Yuba Plays the Rhumba on the Tuba"*? That song was released in 1931! How about a song from 1949 called, *"He's a Real Gone Guy"*? What does "He's a real gone guy" mean?

Did you know that Vic Damone's original name was Vito Farinola?

The Andrews Sisters had a hit song called *"Boogie Woogie Bugle _ _ _ (Boy)."*

Nat "King" Cole sang a song about a famous work of art called the "Mona _ _ _ _ (Lisa)."

What singer is known for his songs *"The Twist"* and *"The Limbo Rock"*? Was it Chubby Fender or Chubby Checker? (Chubby Checker) Did you ever do the Limbo?

Napoleon

1. Did Napoleon Bonaparte begin his military career at age 16? (Yes)
2. Did Napoleon gain fame as a general in the French Revolution or the American Revolution? (French Revolution)
3. In Paris in 1804, Napoleon crowned himself Emperor at the Cathedral of Notre _ _ _ _ (Dame).
4. Was Napoleon Bonaparte Emperor of England or France? (France)
5. Was Napoleon married to Alexandra or Josephine? (Josephine)
6. Was Napoleon exiled to the island of Corfu or Elba? (Elba)
7. Napoleon was defeated at the Battle of Water_ _ _ (loo).
8. Did Napoleon once say, "Never interrupt your enemy when he is making a mistake"? (Yes)

Washington, D.C.

1. Is Washington, D.C. the capital of the United States? (Yes)
2. Did you know that Washington, D.C. was named in honor of George Washington and Christopher Columbus?
3. Does "D.C." stand for District of Congress or District of Columbia? (District of Columbia)
4. Is the long strip of land between the Capitol Building and the Washington Monument called Liberty Park or The Mall? (The Mall)
5. Which river runs through the District of Columbia: the Potomac River or the Mississippi River? (Potomac River)
6. Which is located in Washington, D.C.: the Smithsonian Institution or the Metropolitan Museum of Art? (Smithsonian Institution)
7. Is it true that you can see the Hope Diamond in Washington, D.C.? (Yes, it's in the National Museum of Natural History.)
8. What large military complex is located in Washington, D.C.? Is it the Pentagon or Fort Knox? (Pentagon)

Fill in the *BLANK*

"Soap Operas"

1. *"Days of Our _ _ _ _ _ (Lives)"*
2. *"One Life to _ _ _ _ (Live)"*
3. *"As the World _ _ _ _ _ (Turns)"*
4. *"All My _ _ _ _ _ _ _ _ (Children)"*
5. *"General _ _ _ _ _ _ _ _ (Hospital)"*
6. *"The Edge of _ _ _ _ _ (Night)"*
7. *"Guiding _ _ _ _ _ (Light)"*
8. *"The Young and the _ _ _ _ _ _ _ _ (Restless)"*
9. *"The Bold and the _ _ _ _ _ _ _ _ _ (Beautiful)"*
10. *"Search for _ _ _ _ _ _ _ _ (Tomorrow)"*

Bird Calls

1. Which bird makes a "caw" sound: a quail or a crow? (Crow)
2. A bird that hoots at night is a wise old _ _ _ (owl).
3. Can parrots learn how to talk? (Yes)
4. Do baby birds make a "peep, peep" sound? (Yes)
5. Which bird makes a "coo" sound: a woodpecker or a dove? (Dove)
6. Early in the morning, roosters sing "cock-a-doodle _ _ _ (doo)."
7. Which bird makes a "quack, quack" sound: a pelican or a duck? (Duck)
8. Do hummingbirds make a chirping sound or a humming sound? (Humming sound)
9. Which bird makes a "cluck, cluck, cluck" sound: an egret or a chicken? (Chicken)
10. Which bird makes a "gobble, gobble" sound: a swan or a turkey? (Turkey)

Fill in the BLANK

What the BUILDER said...

1. You hit the nail on the _ _ _ _ (head).
2. People who live in glass houses shouldn't throw _ _ _ _ _ _ (stones).
3. Rome wasn't built in a _ _ _ (day).
4. For want of a nail, the kingdom was _ _ _ _ (lost).
5. You can't fit a round peg into a square _ _ _ _ (hole).
6. Good fences make good _ _ _ _ _ _ _ _ _ (neighbors).
7. There's always room at the _ _ _ (top).
8. Fighting tooth and _ _ _ _ (nail).
9. When I'm done here, I'm going to paint the town _ _ _ (red).
10. It hit me like a ton of _ _ _ _ _ _ (bricks).

Catalog Instructions

The next two pages contain a fictitious mail-order catalog. The object of the activity is to converse and "shop" with your PAL.

Sample questions for the activity are provided below.

- Do you like to look at catalogs?
- We just received a mail-order catalog. Should we order a gift for (insert name)?
- How much should we spend on a gift?
- Which items do you think (name) would like?
- Should we have the items shipped directly to (name) or have them shipped here where we can wrap them first?
- Should we enclose a gift card? What should it say?
- Which items are new?
- Which items are on sale?
- What do you think of the prices?
- What is the cheapest item?
- What is the most expensive item?
- Is (pick an item) a good buy?
- Which items would you like to order for yourself?
- Let's fill out the order form. (If your PAL is unable to fill out the order form, see if you can verbally elicit the information the form asks for.)
- Would you like me to bring you some more catalogs?

Acme's Sweet Treats

~ Serving you since 1926.

NEW

Jelly Candies
$7.99

Candy in Crystal Bowl
$15.99

Vanilla Inside!

Fruit Basket
$12.99

NEW

Licorice
$3.00

Chocolate Cake
$10.99

Assortment of
Tarts
$14.99

Assorted
Chocolates
$12.99

Honey Nuts
$4.00

48

CLEARANCE AISLE

Basket of Grapes
$14.00
Sale $11.99

Chocolate Pieces
$12.99
Sale $9.99

Candied Apple
$2.00
Sale $1.50

Cookies
$8.00
Sale $6.99

Deluxe Cake
$18.99
Sale $15.99

Order Now!

Name: _____

Address: _____

City: _____ State: _____ Zip: _____

Item: _____ Qty: _____ Price: _____

Item: _____ Qty: _____ Price: _____

Item: _____ Qty: _____ Price: _____

Shipping: $6.00

**Order $50.00 or more in merchandise and receive free shipping!

Total: _____

Sing Along

"The Star-Spangled Banner"

by Francis Scott Key

Oh, say, can you see, by the dawn's early _ _ _ _ _ (light),
What so proudly we hailed at the twilight's last _ _ _ _ _ _ _ _ (gleaming)?
Whose broad stripes and bright stars, through the perilous _ _ _ _ _ (fight),
O'er the ramparts we watched, were so gallantly _ _ _ _ _ _ _ _ _ (streaming)?

And the rockets red glare, the bombs bursting in _ _ _ (air),
Gave proof through the night that our flag was still _ _ _ _ _ _ (there).
Oh, say, does that star-spangled banner yet _ _ _ _ (wave),
O'er the land of the free and the home of the _ _ _ _ _ (brave)?

Now Starring Grace Kelly

1. Grace Kelly's first movie with Alfred Hitchcock was *"Dial M for _ _ _ _ _ _ (Murder)."*
2. In 1954, Grace Kelly co-starred with Cary Grant in *"To Catch A _ _ _ _ _ (Thief)."*
3. Grace Kelly was in a suspenseful movie titled *"Rear Window"* directed by Alfred _ _ _ _ _ _ _ _ _ (Hitchcock).
4. Was Grace Kelly a brunette or a blonde? (Blonde)
5. Did Grace Kelly marry Prince Ranier of Monaco? (Yes, in 1956.)
6. When Grace Kelly married Prince Ranier, she became a _ _ _ _ _ _ _ _ (princess).
7. Did you watch Grace Kelly's wedding to Prince Ranier on TV?
8. Did Grace Kelly give up acting when she married Prince Ranier? (Yes)
9. Grace Kelly was in a movie called *"High Society"* which also starred Bing _ _ _ _ _ _ _ (Crosby).
10. For her role in *"The Country Girl,"* Grace Kelly won an Academy _ _ _ _ _ (Award).

Dear Walt,

My car has air-conditioning but lately, it's not putting out cold air. What could be the problem?

Sincerely, Joe

What advice do **YOU** have for Joe?

A. Do you think Joe's air conditioner isn't working because it has a bad compressor?
B. Should Joe add more freon to the air conditioner?
C. Should Joe check the air conditioner belts to make sure they are working properly?
D. Should Joe have a mechanic check out his car's air conditioner?
E. Should Joe trade in his car?

February

Walt's Auto Advice

The First Walk on the Moon

1. Was the first person to walk on the moon an American astronaut or a Russian cosmonaut? (American astronaut)
2. The first man to walk on the moon was Astronaut Neil _ _ _ _ _ _ _ _ _ (Armstrong).
3. When the lunar module touched down on the moon, Neil Armstrong said, "The Eagle has _ _ _ _ _ _ (landed)."
4. Were Neil Armstrong's first steps on the moon televised? (Yes) Did you watch the moon landing on TV?
5. As Neil Armstrong took his first steps, he said "That's one small step for a man, one giant leap for _ _ _ _ _ _ _ (mankind)."
6. Neil Armstrong's fellow astronaut and the second man to walk on the moon was Buzz _ _ _ _ _ _ (Aldrin.)

Who Am I?

1. Who said "Hi-yo Silver"? (The Lone Ranger)
2. Who said "To the moon, Alice"? (Ralph Kramden)
3. Who gave the Gettysburg address? (Abraham Lincoln)
4. Who invented the lightning rod and the Franklin stove? (Benjamin Franklin)
5. Who played Zorba the Greek in the movies? (Anthony Quinn)
6. Who was John F. Kennedy's wife? (Jacqueline Kennedy)
7. Who was the red-headed comedienne who did skits with Harvey Korman and Tim Conway? (Carol Burnett)
8. Who was President James Madison's wife? (Dolley Madison)
9. Who painted the Mona Lisa? (Leonardo da Vinci)
10. Who wrote the book "The Cat in the Hat"? (Dr. Seuss)

Brush Up On Art!

Have you seen the painting called "Whistler's Mother"? James McNeill Whistler painted it in 1871, however he called it "Arrangement in Grey and Black." Most Victorians didn't like that name. After all, a painting has to be <u>about</u> something they said. "Who is it?" they wanted to know. So Whistler renamed his picture "Arrangement in Grey and Black: Portrait of the Artist's Mother." Apparently no one liked that name either… too many words! To this day, people persist in calling it simply "Whistler's Mother."

The "Whistler's Mother" painting is now owned by the French government and hangs in a Paris museum.

Did you know that before he took up painting seriously, Whistler attended the Military Academy at West Point for several years? In later life he liked to say that had he not failed the chemistry exam, he could have been a great general. Who knows? Perhaps if this had come to pass, he would have made a picture called "Whistler's Horse" instead!

LET'S DINE OUT

"The Chinese Restaurant"

1. Would you like to start with a cup of hot tea?
2. For an appetizer would you rather have egg
    rolls or crab puffs?
3. Would you like some egg drop soup or some wonton soup?
4. Would you like to try the restaurant's famous Peking duck?
5. Would you like to order sesame chicken? Do you like it spicy or mild?
6. Would you like chow mein or some sweet and sour pork?
7. Do you want fried rice or plain, steamed rice?
8. What kind of vegetable would you like: broccoli or snow peas?
9. Would you like to eat your Chinese meal with a fork or with chopsticks?
10. How many fortune cookies would you like for dessert?

TV Trivia "Game Shows"

1. Do you remember a game show called *"Wheel of _ _ _ _ _ _ _ _ (Fortune)"*?
2. The letter-turning hostess of *"Wheel of Fortune"* is Vanna _ _ _ _ _ (White).
3. *"Wheel of Fortune"* was created by Merv _ _ _ _ _ _ _ (Griffin).
4. Thanks to *"Wheel of Fortune,"* host Pat Sajak has a star on the Hollywood
    Walk of _ _ _ _ (Fame).
5. Do *"Wheel of Fortune"* players have to buy consonants or vowels? (Vowels)
6. "You're the next contestant on *"The Price is _ _ _ _ _ (Right)."*
7. Who is the host of *"The Price is Right"*? Is it Bob Eubanks or Bob Barker?
    (Bob Barker)
8. *"The Price is Right"* contestants are invited to "Come on _ _ _ _ (down)."
9. Are *"The Price is Right"* models known as "Barker's Babes" or "Barker's
    Beauties"? (Barker's Beauties)
10. "Will the real John Smith please stand up" was a line you might hear on a game
    show called *"To Tell the _ _ _ _ _ (Truth)."*

"The Model T"

1. Is the Model T a Chevrolet or a Ford? (Ford)
2. Have you ever driven a Model T? Did you ever own a Model T?
3. Is the top speed of a Model T 45 miles per hour or 75 miles per hour? (45 miles per hour)
4. Does a Model T have to be started with a hand crank? (Yes)
5. In the old days, were some horses frightened when a Model T passed them on the road? (Yes)
6. Did a Model T sold after 1926 have an electric starter? (Yes)
7. How many miles per gallon does a Model T get? (About 25)
8. Does a Model T have a horn that makes a sound like "Ah-ooh-ga"? (Yes)
9. In the old days, when riding in an open-air Model T, did people wear dusters over their clothes to keep them clean? (Yes)
10. Who invented the Model T? Was it Henry Ford or Henry Kissinger? (Henry Ford)
11. The Model T was the first car to be made on an assembly _ _ _ _ (line).
12. Was the first Model T assembled in Philadelphia or Detroit? (Detroit)
13. Did you know that in 1914, a Model T could be assembled in 93 minutes?
14. In 1924, Ford produced its ten millionth Model T. To mark the occasion, the car was driven from New York to San _ _ _ _ _ _ _ _ _ (Francisco).
15. Between 1915 and 1925, the Model T was only available in one color. Was it black or gray? (Black)
16. Was the Model T considered the first affordable automobile? (Yes)
17. In 1908, did the Model T sell for $450 or $850? ($850)
18. Do you think you could buy a Model T for $850 today?
19. The Model T was also called a "Flivver" or a "Tin _ _ _ _ _ _ (Lizzie)."
20. Did the Model T come in both open-air and hardtop versions? (Yes)
21. Does the Model T motor have 4 cylinders or 8 cylinders? (4 cylinders)
22. Is the Model T still being made today? (No, production ended in 1927.)

All About Me
Playing Cards

1. Do you like to play cards?
2. What is your favorite card game?
3. Who taught you how to play cards? Did your family play card games together?
4. Have you ever played poker? Are you good at keeping a poker face? Did you ever belong to a regular poker group?
5. Have you ever played bridge? Does it take a lot of practice to be a good bridge player? Did you ever play in a bridge tournament?
6. Have you ever played pinochle? Do you like to play with a single deck or a double deck? Did you ever "shoot the moon"?
7. Do you like to play rummy? Who do you like to play rummy with?
8. Do you ever play solitaire? Do you win most of the time?
9. Do you ever invite friends over to play cards? What card games do you play with your friends?
10. Are you good at shuffling cards? Can you demonstrate for me?

Lear's Limericks

There was a young lady whose chin,
Resembled the point of a pin;
So she had it made sharp,
And purchased a harp,
And played several tunes with her chin.

There was an old man with a beard,
Who said, 'It is just as I feared!
Two owls and a hen,
Four larks and a wren,
Have all built their nests in my beard!'

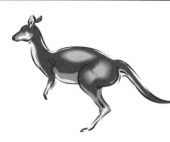

Let's Plan a Day Trip to Melbourne, AUSTRALIA

Melbourne, Australia has over 1200 acres of parks and gardens within 2 miles of the downtown area. Would you like to go strolling in one of the parks?

The Queen Victoria Market in Melbourne was built in 1878. You can buy meat, fish, vegetables, fruit, clothing, arts and crafts, and more. Would you like to shop in the market?

Would you like to stop at the Melbourne Zoo to see the koala bears?

Do you like to gamble? Would you like to visit Melbourne's Crown Casino? What kind of gambling would you like to do?

Australia is famous for its opals. Would you like to see a demonstration of how opals are mined and cut? Would you be interested in shopping for some opal jewelry to take home as a souvenir?

Famous Quotes

Some people ask the secret of our long marriage. We take time to go to a restaurant two times a week. A little candlelight, dinner, soft music, and dancing. She goes Tuesdays, I go Fridays.
-- Henny Youngman

Find a job that you love and you'll never work a day in your life.
-- John P. Grier

Television brings the family into the same room so that they can ignore each other close together. -- Anonymous

Road Trip

1. Did you know that the 17 stars on the Ohio state flag signify that Ohio was the 17th state to be admitted to the Union?
2. Did you know that the name "Ohio" comes from an Iroquois Indian word that means "something great"?
3. Ohio is nicknamed the Buckeye State. Is a buckeye a tree or a flower? (Tree)
4. Does Ohio have lots of rolling plains? (Yes)
5. Two airplane inventors grew up in Dayton, Ohio. Their names were Orville and Wilbur _ _ _ _ _ _ (Wright).
6. The 18th President of the United States was also from Ohio. His name was Ulysses S. _ _ _ _ _ (Grant).
7. Does Ohio border Kentucky? (Yes)
8. Did you know that actor Clark Gable grew up in Ohio?

Under the Hood

1. The strength of a car engine is called horse _ _ _ _ _ (power).
2. The oil in a car is stored in the oil _ _ _ (pan).
3. The oil can be checked with a dip _ _ _ _ _ (stick).
4. If the oil in a car is black, it might be time for an oil _ _ _ _ _ _ (change).
5. A car with a stick shift has a manual trans _ _ _ _ _ _ _ (mission).
6. A car with power steering has a master _ _ _ _ _ _ _ _ (cylinder).
7. A car with eight cylinders is called a V_ (8).
8. For every cylinder, there is a spark _ _ _ _ (plug).
9. Sometimes an engine can blow a _ _ _ _ _ _ (gasket).
10. A souped-up car is sometimes called a hot _ _ _ (rod).

Do you prefer a V8 engine or a 4-banger?

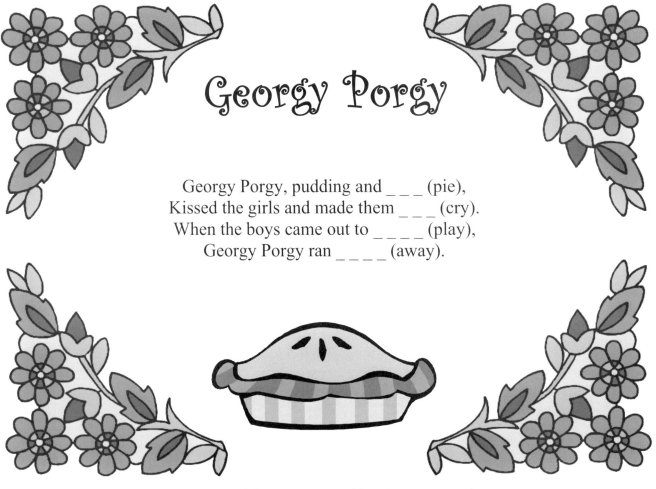

Georgy Porgy

Georgy Porgy, pudding and _ _ _ (pie),
Kissed the girls and made them _ _ _ (cry).
When the boys came out to _ _ _ _ (play),
Georgy Porgy ran _ _ _ _ (away).

58

Under the Sea

"Puffer Fish"

1. Did you know there are over 100 types of puffer fish?
2. Do most puffer fish live in cold water or warm, tropical water? (Tropical water)
3. Can a puffer fish inflate its body like a balloon? (Yes)
4. Did you know that a puffer fish inflates its body by swallowing water?
5. Do puffer fish puff up to scare bigger fish away? (Yes)
6. Can puffer fish swim very fast when they're puffed up? (No, when puffed up their speed is slowed by about half.)
7. Are puffer fish considered a delicacy in Japan? (Yes)
8. Did you know that puffer fish are poisonous unless properly cooked?

Ireland

Let's Go Globetrotting!

1. Is Ireland an island? (Yes)
2. What plant is most associated with Ireland: the shamrock or the poppy? (Shamrock)
3. Blarney Castle is a famous tourist stop. Is kissing the Blarney Stone supposed to make you lucky or give you the gift of gab? (Gift of gab)
4. Did you know it's traditional to kiss the Blarney Stone while you are held upside-down?
5. Jonathan Swift was a popular Irish writer. Did he write *"Gulliver's Travels"* or *"Oliver Twist"*? (*"Gulliver's Travels"*)
6. In Ireland, do people celebrate the Fourth of July or St. Patrick's Day? (St. Patrick's Day)
7. The famous Guinness brand originated in Dublin, Ireland. Is Guinness a brand of beer or whiskey? (Beer)

1. In 1934, Roy Rogers formed a musical group called The Sons of the
    _ _ _ _ _ _ _ _ (Pioneers).

2. The Sons of the Pioneers had a famous song titled *"Tumbling
    _ _ _ _ _ _ _ _ _ _ _ (Tumbleweeds)."*

3. The first movie Roy Rogers appeared in was titled *"Rhythm on the
    Range."* It was filmed in 1936 and starred Martha Raye and
    Bing _ _ _ _ _ _ (Crosby).

4. Roy Rogers was married to Dale _ _ _ _ _ (Evans).

5. Roy Rogers had the "Smartest Horse in the Movies." Was
    his name Bucky or Trigger? (Trigger)

6. Was Roy Rogers known as the "King of the Cowboys"?
    (Yes)

7. Roy Rogers sang a song called *"Don't Fence Me _ _ (In)."*

8. Did you know that Roy Rogers once received 78,852 fan
    letters in a single day?

9. Did you know that Roy Rogers's real name was Leonard
    Slye? Leonard used the name of his childhood dentist, Roy
    Rogers, for his stage name.

10. At the end of every Roy Rogers show, Roy and Dale sang
    "Happy trails to _ _ _ (you)."

Heehaw!

61

Fill in the *BLANK*

What the CLOCKMAKER said...

1. You got here just in the nick of _ _ _ _ (time).
2. I'll have that done for you in two shakes of a lamb's _ _ _ _ (tail).
3. It happened in the twinkling of an _ _ _ (eye).
4. Only time will _ _ _ _ (tell).
5. Time is of the _ _ _ _ _ _ _ (essence).
6. My work will stand the test of _ _ _ _ (time).
7. I wouldn't give him the time of _ _ _ (day).
8. There's no time like the _ _ _ _ _ _ _ (present).
9. She's got a face that could stop a _ _ _ _ _ _ (clock).
10. It's a sign of the _ _ _ _ _ (times).

Now Starring Fred Astaire & Ginger Rogers

1. A famous dancing couple of the 1930's and 40's was Fred Astaire and Ginger _ _ _ _ _ _ (Rogers).
2. Was Ginger's real name "Virginia"? (Yes, she was given the nickname "Ginger" by a young cousin who couldn't pronounce "Virginia" correctly.)
3. Was Fred Astaire's nickname for Ginger Rogers "Feathers"? (Yes)
4. Ginger Rogers made many movies without Fred Astaire. In one of them, she had 3 men vying for her attention. The movie was titled *"Tom, Dick and _ _ _ _ _ (Harry)."*
5. Fred Astaire was often seen elegantly dressed in a top hat, white tie, and _ _ _ _ _ (tails).
6. Fred Astaire sang a song that included the line "When we're out together dancing cheek to _ _ _ _ _ (cheek)."
7. Did Fred Astaire ever receive an Academy Award for his dancing? (Yes, he received a special award in 1949.)
8. Were Fred Astaire's legs insured for one million dollars? (Yes)

Let's Talk About the Picture

"The Taj Mahal"

Show the picture to your PAL while asking these questions:

1. Does the Taj Mahal have a flat roof or a domed roof? (Domed roof)
2. What color is the Taj Mahal? (White/cream)
3. Is the design of the Taj Mahal symmetrical? (Yes)
4. In the photo, is there a crowd of people at the Taj Mahal? (Yes)
5. Is there a reflecting pool of water in front of the Taj Mahal? (Yes)
6. In the photo, is it a cloudy day at the Taj Mahal? (No)

Did you know...

1. The Taj Mahal is located on a river bank in India, and it's a wonder of the modern world.
2. The Taj Mahal was built by the Emperor Shah Jahan in the 17th century.
3. The Emperor's wife, Mumtaz, died during the birth of their 14th child. The grief-stricken Emperor had the Taj Mahal built as a tomb for Mumtaz.
5. The Taj Mahal is built entirely of white marble.
6. Inside and out, the marble is inlaid with semi-precious stones and gems in the shapes of leaves and flowers.
7. When the emperor died, he was buried in the Taj Mahal also.
8. Mumtaz is at the center of the tomb. The emperor is off to one side. Both of the cenotaphs are elaborately jeweled.
9. The Taj Mahal took 22 years to complete.

65

All About Me

Remembering Mother

1. What was your mother's name? What did you call your mother? Did she have a nickname for you?
2. What did your mother look like? Did she wear glasses? What color was her hair?
3. Where was your mother born?
4. Did your mother work outside the home? What job(s) did she have?
5. Did you ever get a spanking from your mother? What did you do to deserve a spanking?
6. Did your mother like to sing or dance? Did she sing songs with you? What did she sing?
7. Did your mother like to talk on the telephone? Who did she talk to?
8. What was the best advice your mother ever gave you?
9. Did you help your Mother with chores?
10. Did your Mother like to listen to the radio? What kind of music did she like?
11. Did you do something special for your mother on Mother's Day? What did you do?
12. Did your mother like to go shopping? Did she take you with her?
13. Did your mother clean your room or did she make you do that?
14. Did your mother like to watch television? What was your mother's favorite television program?
15. Did your mother tuck you into bed every night? Did she read you a bedtime story?
16. Did your mother like to cook? Did she wear an apron? What was your favorite dish?
17. Did your mother bake you a cake on your birthday?
18. Did your mother like to sew? Did your mother make your clothes?
19. When your mother did the laundry did she hang the clothes on a clothes line? Did you help her?
20. What did you love most about your mother?

Football Quiz

1. A referee starts a football game with a coin _ _ _ _ (toss).
2. At the beginning of a football game, is the football put into play with a kickoff? (Yes)
3. A football field is divided by the 50-yard _ _ _ _ (line).
4. At each extreme of the football field there is an end _ _ _ _ (zone).
5. Are the best seats for watching football at the 50-yard line? (Yes)
6. A football game is divided into four quarters. Are they 30 minutes or 15 minutes each? (15 minutes)
7. If neither team is ahead after the 4th quarter, a football game goes into over_ _ _ _ (time).
8. A football referee's uniform is black and _ _ _ _ _ _ (white).
9. Football coaches sometimes call for a time_ _ _ (out).
10. After the second quarter of a football game, there is half-_ _ _ _ (time).

MOVIE TRIVIA
"The Sound of Music"

1. "The Sound of Music" starred Julie _ _ _ _ _ _ _ (Andrews).
2. "The hills are alive with the sound of _ _ _ _ _ (music)."
3. "How do you solve a problem like _ _ _ _ _ (Maria)?"
4. How many children were in the Von Trapp family? (7)
5. "Raindrops on roses and whiskers on _ _ _ _ _ _ (kittens)."
6. Was "The Sound of Music" set in Canada or in Austria? (Austria)
7. "You are sixteen, going on _ _ _ _ _ _ _ (seventeen)."
8. "When the Lord closes a door, somewhere he opens a _ _ _ _ _ _ (window)."
9. "Somewhere in my youth or childhood I must have done something _ _ _ _ (good)."
10. The governess gave the children a singing lesson starting with "do-re-_ _ (mi)."

…Have you ever been so happy you wanted to burst out singing?

Dear Ruth,

Last week, my next-door neighbor came over to visit with her two children, ages 7 and 10. While Helen and I were talking, the 2 children were running all around the living room and jumping on my white sofa. They left dirty shoe smudges on it. I was polite and pretended not to notice. Should I have handled it differently?

Sincerely, Phyllis

Ruth's Advice About Children!

What do **YOU** think Phyllis should have done?

A.   Should Phyllis have asked Helen and her children to leave immediately?
B.   Should Phyllis have spanked Helen's children and sent them outside?
C.   Should Phyllis have asked Helen to pay for cleaning the sofa?
D.   Should Phyllis cover her sofas the next time children come to visit?

Help Wanted: School Bus Driver

1.   Would you like a job driving a school bus?
2.   Would you be willing to drive the school bus for a salary of $10 an hour?
3.   Would you mind getting up very early to drive the school bus?
4.   Have you ever taken a defensive driving course?
5.   Do you like children?
6.   Would you help small children get on and off the bus?
7.   How would you deal with a child who got too rowdy on the bus?
8.   Would you stop the bus at railroad crossings and make sure it was safe to cross?
9.   Would you allow children to stick their arms and heads out of the window while the bus was moving?
10.   Would you be available to drive the school bus on some field trips?
11.   What would you do if you got back to the school and found a child sound asleep at the back of the bus?
12.   What would you enjoy most about driving a school bus?

SIGNS OF THE ZODIAC

Aquarius (Jan 21 – Feb 19) is entertaining, honest, and rebellious!

Was Abraham Lincoln honest?	(b. Feb 12, 1809)
Was James Dean rebellious?	(b. Feb 8, 1931)

Pisces (Feb 20 – Mar 20) is imaginative, intuitive, and sensitive!

Was Albert Einstein intuitive?	(b. Mar 14, 1879)
Was Michelangelo a sensitive artist?	(b. Mar 6, 1475)

Aries (Mar 21 – Apr 19) is adventurous, enthusiastic, and a bit of a daredevil!

Was Howard Cosell an enthusiastic sports announcer?	(b. Mar 25, 1918)
Was Harry Houdini a daredevil?	(b. Mar 24, 1874)

Taurus (Apr 20 – May 21) is warm-hearted, determined, and reliable!

Was General Ulysses S. Grant determined to win the Civil War?	(b. Apr 27, 1822)
Could you rely upon Gary Cooper to give a good performance?	(b. May 7, 1901)

Gemini (May 22 – Jun 21) is witty, youthful, and intellectual!

Were the Dionne quintuplets youthful and lively?	(b. May 28, 1934)
Is Henry Kissinger intellectual?	(b. May 27, 1923)

Cancer (Jun 22 – Jul 23) is emotional, imaginative, and sympathetic!

Was Ernest Hemingway imaginative?	(b. Jul 21, 1899)
Was Art Linkletter a sympathetic listener when he interviewed children?	(b. Jul 17, 1912)

SIGNS OF THE ZODIAC

Leo (Jul 24 – Aug 23) is extroverted, self-confident, and a natural leader!

Was Lucille Ball an extrovert?   (b. Aug 6, 1911)
Was Amelia Earhart a self-confident pilot?   (b. Jul 24, 1897)

Virgo (Aug 24 – Sep 23) is reserved, meticulous, and reliable!

Was Agatha Christie meticulous when   (b. Sep 15, 1890)
  she wrote her murder mysteries?
Was Paul Harvey a reliable reporter   (b. Sep 4, 1918)
  of the news?

Libra (Sep 24 – Oct 22) is easy-going, romantic, and charming!

Was Ed Sullivan an easy-going TV host?   (b. Sep 28, 1901)
Was Helen Hayes charming?   (b. Oct 10, 1900)

Scorpio (Oct 23 – Nov 22) is powerful, determined, and emotional!

Was Theodore Roosevelt powerful?   (b. Oct 27, 1858)
Was Dr. Jonas Salk determined to find   (b. Oct 28, 1914)
  a polio vaccine?

Sagittarius (Nov 23 – Dec 21) is good-humored, freedom-loving, and energetic!

Was Winston Churchill freedom-loving?   (b. Nov 30, 1874)
Was Sammy Davis, Jr. an energetic dancer? (b. Dec 8, 1925)

Capricorn (Dec 22 – Jan 20) is shrewd, disciplined, and trustworthy!

Was Aristotle Onassis a shrewd   (b. Jan 15, 1906)
  businessman?
Was Paul Revere trustworthy?   (b. Jan 1, 1735)

Classified Ads

Circle the ads you're interested in.

MONDAY NIGHT AUCTION! Speedboat with outboard motor. Includes trailer and water skiing equipment. Auction starts promptly at 7 pm in the old warehouse building on Main St.

For Sale: Refrigerator, side by side, almond color, 4 shelves, like new, $140. Call Monica.

VOLUNTEER NEEDED! Need a volunteer to teach golf to young people, about 2 hours on Saturdays for the next 8 weeks. Call Larry at the golf course if interested in donating your time.

For sale: Used mattress and box springs. Like new. $100. Call Nellie.

For sale: Rocking chair, solid wood with light blue cushion. Very comfortable, $45. Call Pat.

Wanted: Someone to help me prepare my tax return. Desperately need help! Willing to pay extra for expert assistance. Please call Jim before April 15.

Woman, 69, 5'3", 135 lbs, seeks fun-loving, financially independent man for travel and companionship. Call Ruth.

Wanted: I'm looking for an oval coffee table for my living room. If you have one you'd like to sell, please call Millie after 6 pm.

Free to good home: Trained parrot named "Polly," 6 years old, talks all the time! Knows many tricks! Beautiful red, blue, & green feathers. Call Denise.

Moving Sale, Saturday only from sunup to sundown. EVERYTHING must go! Furniture, tools, dishes and more! Corner of Maple and 3rd.

Sing Along

"The Farmer in the Dell"

The farmer in the dell
The farmer in the dell
Hi-ho, the derry-o
The farmer in the dell

The farmer takes a wife
The farmer takes a wife
Hi-ho, the derry-o
The farmer takes a wife

The wife takes a child
The wife takes a child
Hi-ho, the derry-o
The wife takes a child

The child takes a nurse
The child takes a nurse
Hi-ho, the derry-o
The child takes a nurse

The nurse takes a cow
The nurse takes a cow
Hi-ho, the derry-o
The nurse takes a cow

The dog takes a cat
The dog takes a cat
Hi-ho, the derry-o
The dog takes a cat

The cat takes a rat
The cat takes a rat
Hi-ho, the derry-o
The cat takes a rat

The rat takes the cheese
The rat takes the cheese
Hi-ho, the derry-o
The rat takes the cheese

The cheese stands alone
The cheese stands alone
Hi-ho, the derry-o
The cheese stands alone

Let's Talk About Ants!

1. Did you know that there are more than 10,000 different kinds of ants?
2. Did you know that all ants can bite but only some can sting?
3. What do you call a group of ants, a herd or a colony? (A colony)
4. Do all ant colonies have at least one queen? (Yes)
5. When ants dig tunnels they create a mound of earth called an ant _ _ _ _ (hill).
6. Did you know that ants can carry up to 20 times their body weight?
7. Do ants use their antennae as feelers? (Yes)
8. Do soldier ants defend their colonies? (Yes)
9. Would a carpenter ant prefer to make a nest in sand or wood? (Wood)
10. Did you know that the average life expectancy of an ant is 60 days?
11. Do worker ants take care of young ants? (Yes)
12. Did you ever have an ant farm? Have you ever been bitten by an ant?

Dear Hazel,

My mother-in-law is coming for a visit next week. No matter how much I clean, it's never good enough for my mother-in-law. If she finds even a speck of dirt, she chides me for being a bad housekeeper. What should I do?

Sincerely, Mary

What do **YOU** think Mary should do?

A. Should Mary spend more time dusting?
B. Should Mary apologize to her mother-in-law for the dust?
C. Should Mary ask her mother-in-law to do the dusting?
D. Should Mary hire a cleaning service?
E. Should Mary stop inviting her mother-in-law for visits?

Road Trip

2 Miles ⟶

1. Did you know that the word "Dakota" is a Sioux Indian word meaning "friends"?
2. Is South Dakota nicknamed the Mount Rushmore State? (Yes)
3. Have you been to Mount Rushmore? Tell me about it.
4. Did you know that the geographic center of the United States is a city in South Dakota called Belle Fourche?
5. South Dakota has an official state insect. It's yellow and black and makes a buzzing sound when it flies. It's called a honey _ _ _ (bee).
6. Is South Dakota famous for its Orange Hills or its Black Hills? (Black Hills)
7. One of South Dakota's famous residents of the 1800's was Laura Ingalls _ _ _ _ _ _ (Wilder).

MOVIE TRIVIA
"Alice in Wonderland"

1. Do you remember an animated Walt Disney movie titled "Alice in Wonder_ _ _ _ (land)"?
2. Alice followed a white rabbit down a rabbit _ _ _ _ (hole).
3. While in the woods, Alice met a caterpillar sitting on a mush_ _ _ _ (room).
4. There was always a big grin on the face of the Cheshire _ _ _ (Cat).
5. Alice had tea with the Mad Hatter and the March _ _ _ _ (Hare).
6. The story of "The Walrus and The Carpenter" was told by Tweedledee and Tweedle_ _ _ (dum)."
7. Alice came upon the garden of the Queen of _ _ _ _ _ _ (Hearts).
8. In the garden, three gardeners were painting the roses _ _ _ (red).
9. The Queen of Hearts shouted, "Off with their _ _ _ _ _ (heads)."
10. Did Alice and the Queen of Hearts play a game of croquet? (Yes)

… Have you ever been as mad as a March hare?

Copyright © 2007 Sunshine & Joy Enterprises   75

Fads and Fashions of the 1920's

1. During the roaring twenties, many women broke the rules of convention. They wore their dresses short, they smoked, and they danced the Charleston. Were these women of the 1920's called hippies or flappers? (Flappers)
2. Flappers liked to accessorize their outfits with long strings of _ _ _ _ _ _ (pearls or beads).
3. Makeup was popular in the 1920's. Flappers often wore bright red lip_ _ _ _ _ (stick).
4. Bobbed hair was all the rage in the 1920's. In the middle of their foreheads, some flappers wore a spit _ _ _ _ (curl).
5. Were flappers more often seen at all-you-can-eat buffets or all-night dance marathons? (Dance marathons)
6. Popular dances of the 1920's were the shimmy and the fox_ _ _ _ (trot).
7. Another form of entertainment in the 1920's was to see how long someone could sit on top of a flag _ _ _ _ (pole).
8. Can you guess what kind of sandwich became famous in 1922? Here's a hint… peanut butter and _ _ _ _ _ _ (jelly).

ANACROSTIC

1.) One European bicycle race is called the Tour de __ __ __ __ __ __ .
                                            1 2 3 4 5 6

2.) A classroom teacher often sits behind a __ __ __ __ .
              7 8 9 10

3.) A child's toy is a spinning __ __ __ .
          11 12 13

4.) A wound takes time to __ __ __ __ .
      14 15 16 17

Caregiver Tip:

___ ___ ___   ___ ___ ___   ___ ___ ___   ___ ___ ___ ___ ___ ___
3 9 10   1 12 2   3 4 7   16 5 5 6 13 11

___ ___ ___ ___
14 8 17 13

William Shakespeare

1. Was William Shakespeare born in the year 1864 or 1564? (1564)
2. Was William Shakespeare born in Spain or England? (England)
3. Is William Shakespeare known as "The Bard of Avon"? (Yes)
4. Did Shakespeare write 10 plays or more than 30 plays? (More than 30)
5. William Shakespeare wrote a play called *"Romeo and _ _ _ _ _ _ (Juliet)."*
6. Is *Romeo and Juliet* a comedy or a tragedy? (Tragedy)
7. Did William Shakespeare ever attend a university? (No)
8. Did William Shakespeare marry a woman named Anne Hathaway? (Yes)
9. Shakespeare's character Hamlet says, "To be, or not to be: that is the _ _ _ _ _ _ _ _ (question)."
10. In addition to writing plays, was Shakespeare an actor? (Yes)
11. Did William Shakespeare perform for Queen Elizabeth I? (Yes)
12. William Shakespeare wrote a play called *"Much Ado About _ _ _ _ _ _ _ (Nothing)."*
13. Have Shakespeare's plays been made into movies? (Yes, many of them.)
14. William Shakespeare wrote a play called *"The Taming of the _ _ _ _ _ (Shrew)."*
15. Did you know that Shakespeare added more than 1700 new words to the English language?
16. William Shakespeare wrote a play called *"A Midsummer Night's _ _ _ _ _ (Dream)."*
17. Was William Shakespeare part owner of the Globe Theatre in London? (Yes)
18. William Shakespeare wrote a play called *"All's Well That Ends _ _ _ _ (Well)."*
19. Did William Shakespeare write a play about Antony and Cleopatra? (Yes)
20. Is it true that Shakespeare is the most quoted author in the English language? (Yes)
21. Did William Shakespeare write a play called *"MacDonald"* or *"Macbeth"*? (*"Macbeth"*)
22. If someone says "The world is my oyster," are they quoting Shakespeare? (Yes)
23. Do you like to read Shakespeare?
24. Did you ever perform in a Shakespeare play? What part did you play?

How Does Your Garden Grow?

1. What tool would you use to dig a small hole, a trowel or a hoe? (Trowel)

2. Do elm trees provide good shade? (Yes)

3. Is broccoli considered a type of fruit or a type of cabbage? (Cabbage)

4. Is it true that pinching a snapdragon makes it look like a real dragon opening its mouth? (Yes)

5. Is an aphid a large insect or a small insect? (Small insect)

6. Do junipers make good landscape plants? (Yes)

7. Is corn harvested in the spring or in late summer? (Late summer)

8. Do zinnias make good cut flowers for flower arrangements? (Yes)

9. When you eat a beet, are you eating the root of the plant or the leaves? (Root)

10. Is it true that tomatoes grow best if they are staked or grown in a cage? (Yes)

11. Do rosemary plants have pale blue flowers? (Yes)

12. Do orange trees have fragrant flowers? (Yes)

Cut-Peel-Wear Stickers

Foxtrot Instructor

Give Me A Wink!

Ask me about my favorite team !

BINGO

Bingo, anyone?

It's My Birthday!

I ♥ My Grandkids

81

Fill in the *BLANK*

Things Dad might have said...

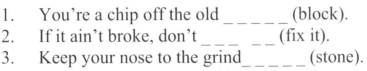

1. You're a chip off the old _ _ _ _ _ (block).
2. If it ain't broke, don't _ _ _ _ _ (fix it).
3. Keep your nose to the grind_ _ _ _ _ (stone).
4. Do as I say, not as I _ _ (do).
5. You've got to stand on your own two _ _ _ _ (feet).
6. If at first you don't succeed, try, try, _ _ _ _ _ (again).
7. Children should be seen and not _ _ _ _ _ (heard).
8. Put your best foot _ _ _ _ _ _ _ (forward).
9. You're eating me out of house and _ _ _ _ (home).
10. Do you think money grows on _ _ _ _ _ (trees)?

Road Trip

OREGON
10 Miles ➡

1. Did you know that the name "Oregon" comes from a French word meaning "hurricane"?
2. Oregon is nicknamed the Beaver State. Have you ever seen a beaver?
3. Crater Lake is in Oregon. Is it the deepest lake in America? (Yes, it is 1,932 feet deep.)
4. Does Oregon produce a lot of lumber? (Yes)
5. Did you know that Oregon has more ghost towns than any other state?
6. Can you go to a self-service gas station in Oregon? (No, all gas stations in Oregon are full service.)
7. Did you know that Oregon has the largest sea lion cave in the world?
8. The thirty-first President of the United States grew up in Oregon. His name was Herbert _ _ _ _ _ _ (Hoover).

Food for Thought

1. Is the inside of a sweet potato green or orange? (Orange)
2. What color is a plum tomato? (Red)
3. Should hot dogs be stored in the pantry or in the refrigerator? (Refrigerator)
4. If a recipe says to "baste the turkey," do you sew it up with thread? (No, basting the turkey means keeping it moist with juice.)
5. Which weighs more: a watermelon or a cantaloupe? (Watermelon)
6. Which pie is more traditional at Thanksgiving: key lime pie or pecan pie? (Pecan pie)
7. Would you put a maraschino cherry on a sundae or in a soup? (Sundae)
8. Which fruit is a deep purple color: mangos or plums? (Plums)
9. Does a slice of pumpkin pie have more calories than an orange? (Yes)
10. Which food can you buy in a can: English muffins or oysters? (Oysters)

Fill in the SONG TITLES

Do You Remember These Songs?

1. *"Put Your Head on My _ _ _ _ _ _ _ _ (Shoulder)"*
2. *"I Don't Want to Set the World on _ _ _ _ (Fire)"*
3. *"Lullaby of _ _ _ _ _ _ _ _ (Broadway)"*
4. *"Strike Up the _ _ _ _ (Band)"*
5. *"Hit the Road _ _ _ _ (Jack)"*
6. *"You're in the Army _ _ _ (Now)"*
7. *"Come Rain or Come _ _ _ _ _ (Shine)"*
8. *"I'm Just Wild About _ _ _ _ _ (Harry)"*
9. *"Tutti _ _ _ _ _ _ (Frutti)"*
10. *"Red Sails in the Sun_ _ _ (set)"*

Comparing
Apples to Oranges

1. What's more expensive: a yacht or a rowboat?
2. What's more faded: a new pair of jeans or an old pair of jeans?
3. What's more gigantic: the Pacific Ocean or Lake Erie?
4. What's more glamorous: a mink stole or a woolen shawl?
5. What's more grandiose: a cottage or a palace?
6. What's more horrible: a pimple or the measles?
7. What's more melodic: a cage full of chickens or a cage full of canaries?
8. What's bigger: a mouse or a rabbit?
9. What's more nauseating: rough seas or calm seas?
10. What's more noxious: ammonia or perfume?
11. What's more nutritious: milk or water?
12. What's more crooked: the Empire State Building or the Leaning Tower of Pisa?

All About Me
My First Job

1. What was your first job? How old were you when you got your first job? Were you nervous on your first day at work?
2. Did you like your boss? What was his/her name?
3. Did you have to get up early in the morning to go to work?
4. Were you ever late for work because you overslept?
5. How did you get to your job? Did you walk, take the bus, or drive?
6. Did you wear a uniform to work? What did it look like? Did it have a hat? Did you wear a nametag?
7. Did you earn a lot of money at your first job?
8. Did you make new friends at your first job?
9. Did you have to punch a time clock? Did they blow a whistle when it was time to go home?
10. How long did you work at your first job? Why did you leave?

Let's Talk About the Picture

"Plymouth Lighthouse"

Show the picture to your PAL while asking these questions:

1. What color is the very top of Plymouth Lighthouse? (Red)
2. What color is the door to Plymouth Lighthouse? (Black)
3. Is there a ladder to climb up to the top of the lighthouse? (Yes)
4. Does Plymouth Lighthouse have a window? (Yes)
5. Is there grass around the lighthouse? (Yes)
6. Is it a cloudy day at the lighthouse? (Yes)

Did you know:..

1. Plymouth Lighthouse is located in Massachusetts. It was built in 1769.
2. The purpose of Plymouth Lighthouse is to guide ships away from dangerous rocks.
3. Plymouth Lighthouse is 39 feet tall and has two lights. The beacon can be seen up to 16 miles away.
4. John Thomas, a general in the American Revolution, was the first keeper of Plymouth Lighthouse.
5. When John Thomas died, his wife Hannah became the first woman lighthouse keeper.
6. A nickname for a lighthouse keeper is a "wickie."
7. Plymouth Lighthouse was destroyed in 1801 by an oil fire. Two octagonal towers were built to replace the old towers.
8. In 1924, one of the octagonal towers was torn down. The remaining tower is now the oldest wooden lighthouse in America.

Let's Go Globetrotting!

Greece

1. Is it true that Greece has well over 1,000 islands? (Yes)

2. Is the highest mountain in Greece called Mount Athens or Mount Olympus? (Mount Olympus)

3. Is the currency of Greece called the euro or the peso? (Euro)

4. Is Greece mostly mountainous or mostly flat? (Mountainous)

5. Is the most famous building of ancient Greece called the Parthenon or the Coliseum? (Parthenon)

6. Do Greek recipes more often call for corn oil or olive oil? (Olive oil)

7. Were Socrates, Plato, and Aristotle famous philosophers of Greece? (Yes)

8. Hippocrates was another famous Greek. Was Hippocrates the father of music or the father of medicine? (Medicine)

9. A famous Greek statue is the Venus de Milo. Is the Venus de Milo missing its arms or legs? (Arms)

10. In Greek mythology, was the god of the sea called Poseidon or Cupid? (Poseidon)

11. Is it true that many English words have their origins in the Greek language? (Yes)

12. Does it ever snow in Greece? (Yes)

Dear Maude,

My husband, Fred, recently got a nice bonus at work. Fred and I have been arguing about how to spend the bonus money. Fred wants to buy a new boat. I want to pay off some bills. What should we do?

Sincerely, June

What's <u>YOUR</u> advice to June and Fred?

A.   Should June let Fred buy the boat he wants?
B.   Should June put her foot down and say, "Fred, if you buy that boat, you'll be looking for another first mate!"
C.   Should Fred say to his wife, "June, I'm the captain in this household and I'm buying a boat with that money!"
D.   Should Fred and June toss a coin to decide how to spend the money?
E.   Should Fred listen to June and agree to pay off their bills?

Cleopatra

1.   Did you know that Cleopatra was born in 69 BC?
2.   Was Cleopatra Egyptian or Greek? (Greek)
3.   Cleopatra and Julius Caesar had one son. Was his name Julius, Jr. or Caesarion? (Caesarion)
4.   After Julius Caesar's death, did Cleopatra marry Mark Antony? (Yes)
5.   Did Mark Antony take his own life when he mistakenly thought Cleopatra was dead? (Yes)
6.   A few days later, did Cleopatra poison herself with a spider bite or a snake bite? (Snake bite)
7.   Was Cleopatra the last Queen of Egypt? (Yes)

Fill-in-the-Drawing

Instructions

1. Put eyebrows on the sun's face.
2. Put more flames around the sun.
3. Put another spot on the butterfly's wing.
4. Put antennae on the butterfly.
5. Finish drawing the cat's left ear.
6. Add whiskers to the cat.
7. Put a tag on the cat's collar.

True or False?

1. Is it true that pigs sweat? (No. Pigs don't have sweat glands. They wallow in water and mud to cool off.)
2. Is it true that more people in the world speak Chinese than any other language? (Yes)
3. Is it true that most people like anchovies on their pizza? (No)
4. Is it true that saber-toothed tigers still roam in the mountains of California? (No. Saber-toothed tigers are extinct.)
5. Is it true that more people call in sick on Monday than any other day of the week? (No. More people call in sick on Friday.)
6. Is it true that raccoons hibernate during the winter? (Yes)
7. Is it true that in Texas, there are towns called Ding Dong, Lollipop, and Sugar Land? (Yes)
8. Is it true that Sir Francis Drake was an explorer from England? (Yes)
9. Is it true that chocolate is the most popular ice cream flavor? (No, vanilla is the most popular ice cream flavor.)
10. Is it true that Hadrian was a Roman emperor? (Yes)

Let's Design Your... Dream Kids!

1. If you could have dream kids, would they be all boys, all girls, or a combination of both?
2. Will your dream kids have good manners and always remember to say "please" and "thank you"?
3. While traveling, will your dream kids repeatedly ask, "Are we there yet?"
4. Will your dream kids have good appetites and eat all their vegetables?
5. Will your dream kids clean their rooms without having to be asked?
6. Will your dream kids do all of their homework?
7. Will your dream kids love to play outside?
8. Will your dream kids ever sass back?
9. Will your dream kids give you any dream grandchildren?
10. What hobbies will your dream kids have?
11. Will your dream kids hide their dirty socks under the bed?
12. Will your dream kids help with household chores?

The Buzz About Beavers

1. Did you know that beavers are the largest rodents in North America?
2. Would you believe a beaver can weigh up to 60 pounds?
3. Beavers live near rivers, lakes, and streams where they like to build _ _ _ _ (dams).
4. Do beavers have bushy tails or flat tails? (Flat tails)
5. Are beavers smooth-skinned or furry? (Furry)
6. Are baby beavers called cats or kits? (Kits)
7. Can a beaver cut down a tree? (Yes, a beaver can chew through a 10-inch diameter tree in a single night!)
8. Is a beaver home called a shack or a lodge? (A lodge)
9. Is the beaver a national symbol of the United States or Canada? (Canada)
10. Do beavers have webbed hind feet? (Yes)
11. Do beavers eat tree bark? (Yes)
12. Have you ever seen a beaver dam? Where?

TV Trivia "The Little Rascals"

1. *"Our Gang"* is also known as *"The Little* _ _ _ _ _ _ _ *(Rascals)."*
2. The skinny, freckle-faced kid with a wild cowlick is Al_ _ _ _ _ (falfa).
3. Alfalfa's relationship with his girlfriend, Darla, is on-again, off-_ _ _ _ _ (again).
4. The gang's dog, Pete the pup, is white with a black circle around his _ _ _ (eye).
5. Which rascal wears a multicolored beanie cap, Spanky or Alfalfa? (Spanky)
6. Does Spanky like to say "Okey-dokey"? (Yes, he popularized that expression.)
7. The rascal with big hair is called Buck_ _ _ _ _ (wheat).
8. Are the little rascals tormented by a bully named Butch? (Yes)
9. Is the littlest rascal named Stymie or Porky? (Stymie)
10. Does Porky often say "O-tay"? (Yes)

...Did you know that Shirley Temple was turned down for a part in *"The Little Rascals"*?

Say When!

1. Was King Tut's tomb discovered in the 1920's or the 1960's? (1920's)
2. Was Mozart born before Liberace? (Yes)
3. Was the automobile invented before the airplane? (Yes)
4. When making toast, do you butter the bread before it goes into the toaster? (No)
5. Which happened first: World War I or World War II? (World War I)
6. Did Rembrandt paint before Picasso? (Yes)
7. Which fad came first: zoot suits or bell-bottom pants? (Zoot suits)
8. Did the Battle of Waterloo take place before World War I? (Yes)
9. Did Marco Polo go exploring before Christopher Columbus did? (Yes)
10. Was Joan of Arc born before Joan Collins? (Yes)
11. Were Thomas Jefferson and George Washington born around the same time? (Yes)
12. Which comes first, the chicken or the egg?

Rainbow Quiz

1. What color are cherries? (Red)
2. If you mix white paint and red paint, will you have pink paint? (Yes)
3. What color is a four-leaf clover? (Green)
4. Is yellow considered to be a warm color? (Yes)
5. Does a rainbow include the color brown? (No)
6. What colors do you see a lot of on the Fourth of July? (Red, white, and blue)
7. If a man waves a white flag during a battle, is he ready to lead a charge or is he surrendering? (Surrendering)
8. What color is pistachio ice cream? (Green)
9. If a friend asked you to paint his new kitchen, what color would you choose?
10. What color was Elvis Presley's 1955 Cadillac, blue or pink? (Pink)

Madrid, Spain

Let's Go Globetrotting!

1. Is Madrid the capital of Spain or Italy? (Spain)

2. Madrid has a famous art museum. Is it the Louvre or the Prado? (Prado)

3. Was Spain's last dictator named Charles de Gaulle or Francisco Franco? (Francisco Franco)

4. Is it true that Spain's best-selling singer, Julio Iglesias, was born in Madrid? (Yes)

5. One of Madrid's more famous residents was Miguel de Cervantes. Was he the author of *"Ivanhoe"* or *"Don Quixote"*? (*"Don Quixote"*)

6. Did Spain's most famous artist, Pablo Picasso, go to art school in Madrid? (Yes, but he never finished his classes.)

7. In Madrid, would you be more likely to see polka dancers or flamenco dancers? (Flamenco dancers)

8. Have you ever been to Madrid? Tell me about it.

Fill in the *BLANK*

RELATIONSHIP ADVICE

1. Take the bitter with the _ _ _ _ _ (sweet).
2. Let bygones be _ _ _ _ _ _ _ (bygones).
3. It's never over 'til its _ _ _ _ (over).
4. Parting is such sweet _ _ _ _ _ _ (sorrow).
5. Don't wear your heart on your _ _ _ _ _ _ (sleeve).
6. The course of true love never did run _ _ _ _ _ _ (smooth).
7. Familiarity breeds _ _ _ _ _ _ _ _ (contempt).
8. Swallow your _ _ _ _ _ (pride).
9. Misery loves _ _ _ _ _ _ _ (company).
10. Absence makes the heart grow _ _ _ _ _ _ (fonder).

Betty's Home Remedies

Dear Betty,

I have a very big problem. My husband snores! It's so loud, I can't sleep at night. Yesterday I was so tired that I fell asleep on the job. My boss said if it happens again, I'll be fired! I don't know where else to turn. What should I do about my husband's snoring?

Sincerely, Janet

What do **YOU** think Janet should do?

A. Should Janet start sleeping in another room?
B. Should Janet make her husband sleep in another room?
C. Should Janet start wearing earplugs?
D. Should Janet wake her husband up every time he starts to snore?
E. Do you have a remedy for snoring?

"Abraham Lincoln"

1. Was Abraham Lincoln born in a one-room log cabin in Kentucky? (Yes, in 1809.)
2. What did Abraham Lincoln look like? Was he short or tall? (Tall) Did Abraham Lincoln have a beard? (Yes)
3. If Abraham Lincoln ran for President today, would you vote for him?
4. Was Abraham Lincoln a Republican or a Democrat? (Republican)
5. Before becoming a politician, was Abraham Lincoln an inventor or a lawyer? (Lawyer)
6. Was the Lincoln automobile named after Abraham Lincoln? (Yes)
7. Does Lincoln's image appear on the penny or the nickel? (Penny)
8. Lincoln gave a famous speech called the Gettysburg _ _ _ _ _ _ _ (Address).
9. Can you finish this line from the Gettysburg Address: "Fourscore and seven years _ _ _ (ago)..."
10. Abraham Lincoln was given the nickname "Honest _ _ _ (Abe)."
11. Where was President Lincoln when he was assassinated? Was he in a restaurant or a theater? (He was in the Ford Theater.)
12. Was Abraham Lincoln president during the Civil War? (Yes)
13. Was President Lincoln elected to a second term? (Yes)
14. Did Abraham Lincoln have a middle name? (No)
15. Was Abraham Lincoln married to Jane Chestnut or Mary Todd? (Mary Todd)
16. Did Abraham Lincoln have four sons or four daughters? (Four sons: Robert, Eddie, Willie and Tad)

Fill in the *Blank*

FICTIONAL PAIRS

1. *"Hansel and _ _ _ _ _ _ (Gretel)"*
2. *"Beauty and the _ _ _ _ _ (Beast)"*
3. *"The Owl and the _ _ _ _ _ _ _ _ (Pussycat)"*
4. *"The Princess and the _ _ _ (Pea)"*
5. *"The Tortoise and the _ _ _ _ (Hare)"*
6. *"Jack and the Bean_ _ _ _ _ (stalk)"*
7. *"Goldilocks and the Three _ _ _ _ _ (Bears)"*
8. *"Raggedy Ann and _ _ _ _ (Andy)"*
9. *"Jack and _ _ _ _ (Jill)"*
10. *"Charlie and the Chocolate _ _ _ _ _ _ _ (Factory)"*

All About Me
Open Wide

1. How old were you when you first went to a dentist?
2. After a visit to the dentist, were you rewarded with a lollipop or a new toothbrush?
3. Did your parents have to remind you to brush your teeth every day? Did you ever brush your teeth with tooth powder?
4. Did you ever pull a tooth by tying a string around it?
5. Did you wear braces when you were a teenager? Were you happy the day you got your braces off?
6. Have you ever had a cavity? How many?
7. Did you ever have a tooth pulled by a dentist?
8. Did you have your wisdom teeth pulled? Do wisdom teeth have anything to do with being smart?
9. Did the dentist ever give you laughing gas?
10. Did you ever have a tooth knocked out? What happened?

Mark Your Calendar!

Wacky (but Real) Dates to Celebrate

January is "It's OK to be Different" Month.
January 16 is National Fig Newton Day.
January 22 is National Hugging Day.
January 30 is Yodel for Your Neighbors Day.

February is Return Carts to the Supermarket Month.
February 2 is Wear Red Day.
February 12 is National Plum Pudding Day.
February 22 is Be Humble Day.

March is National Noodle Month.
The first week in March is Return Borrowed Books Week.
March 4 is National Dance the Waltz Day.
March 22 is International Goof Off Day.

April is Daisy Flower Month.
The first Monday in April is Sweet Potato Day.
April 13 is Blame Someone Else Day.
April 25 is National Zucchini Bread Day.

May is National Barbecue Month.
May 3 is National Scrapbook Day.
May 11 is Eat What You Want Day.
May 24 is Asparagus Day.

June is National Rose Month.
June 10 is National Yo-Yo Day.
June 20 is Ice Cream Soda Day.
June 28 is Let it Go Day (Whatever is bothering you, let it go!)

July is National Hotdog Month.
July 6 is National Fried Chicken Day.
July 23 is National "Hot Enough for Ya?" Day.
July 27 is Take Your Pants for a Walk Day.

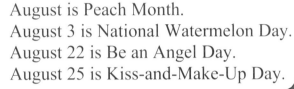

August is Peach Month.
August 3 is National Watermelon Day.
August 22 is Be an Angel Day.
August 25 is Kiss-and-Make-Up Day.

September is International Square Dance Month.
September 5 is Be Late for Something Day.
September 23 is Checkers Day.
September 28 is Love Note Day.

October is National Pizza Month.
October 3 is National Denim Day.
October 15 is Mushroom Day.
October 26 is National Sleep In Day.

November is National Raisin Bread Month.
November 2 is National Deviled Egg Day.
November 14 is Loosen Up, Lighten Up Day.
November 28 is French Toast Day.

December is Write to a Friend Month.
December 1 is Eat a Red Apple Day.
December 12 is National Ding-a-ling Day.
December 18 is Play Bingo Day.

Helpful Hints for the Greeting Card Activity

The greeting cards combine a stimulating activity with a means of letting your PAL's friends and family know that they are remembered. Don't be embarrassed to mail a card that contains merely lines, scribbles, or dots. A card that is less than perfect, but comes from the heart, will touch the recipient more than any slick, store-bought card could ever do. It's the thought that counts!

What if my PAL:

Doesn't know what to do with the card.	Make gentle verbal suggestions if your PAL is unsure what to do next. Nonverbal cues such as handing your PAL a colored pencil may also encourage participation.
Is unable to color.	Lines, dots, numbers, or any mark at all is okay. The object is to encourage participation to whatever extent your PAL is able.
Wants to color the sky fuchsia.	Hold the pencils and ask, "What color do you think the sky should be?" If the answer isn't blue, just go with the flow. Maybe you're assisting the next Picasso!
Becomes bored or distracted.	The card doesn't have to be finished in one session. If your PAL loses interest, set the activity aside and resume it later.
Can't write a message.	A signature or mark of any kind from your PAL is acceptable. Or, suggest possible messages. Write down the one your PAL likes.

REMEMBER:

~ The spirit of the activity should be light and fun.
~ Praise and admire your PAL's work, no matter what the result.
~ There is no wrong way to decorate the cards.
~ Criticism is counterproductive.
~ Resist any temptation to alter your PAL's efforts.

A little birdie told me it's your birthday.

Cut along dotted line. Color as desired. Write a message. Fold in half and seal with a sticker. Add an address and a stamp. Mail.

Happy Birthday

From:

Place
Stamp
Here

To:

Not too much happening around here. How are you?

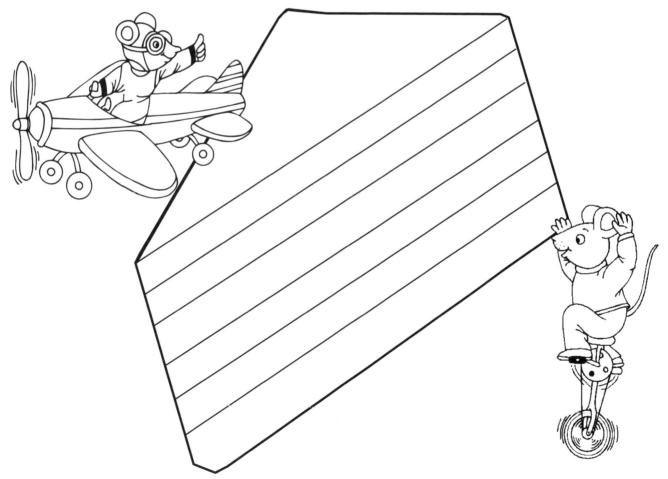

From:

Place
Stamp
Here

To:

Flash Card Instructions

(Flash cards begin on page 113.)

Sunshine and Joy's flash cards can be saved and reused. Cut the flash card pages along the dotted black lines to form eight flash cards. You can perform several activities with the flash cards:

Option 1: Point to the picture on each flash card and ask your PAL to identify it.

Option 2: Point to the word that describes the picture and ask your PAL to read it to you.

Option 3: Mix up the cards and lay them out in front of your PAL. Ask your PAL to match the objects.

Option 4: Ask your PAL which object(s) would be found in the kitchen, bathroom, etc.

Option 5: Ask your PAL to identify the objects by shape or color, for example, "Which object is pink?"

Sunshine Strip Instructions

Sunshine Strips can be used again and again. Cut the Sunshine Strip page along the solid black lines to form three Sunshine Strips.

Each Sunshine Strip contains two pictures. Face your PAL. Hold up one Sunshine Strip so that the pictures can easily be seen by your PAL. The back of each strip contains questions related to the pictures or an instruction to point to one of the two objects. Read each item to your PAL.

108

Sunshine Strips

Cut along solid black lines to form three Sunshine Strips

1) Which item would you use to sharpen a pencil?

2) Which item would you use to hold paper in place?

3) Which item is rectangular?

4) Point to the clipboard.

5) Which item has a handle to turn?

6) Point to the pencil sharpener.

7) Which item would you use as a surface to write on?

1) Which item would hold your files?

2) Which item tells you what time it is?

3) Point to the file cabinet.

4) Point to the clock.

5) How many drawers does the file cabinet have?

6) Does the clock say it's time for lunch?

7) Which item is round?

1) Which item would you use to cut paper?

2) Which item would you use to add numbers?

3) Point to the scissors.

4) Which item would an accountant use all day long?

5) Which item has two sharp blades?

6) Point to the calculator.

7) Which item requires you to push buttons?

Sunshine Strips

Cut along solid black lines to form three Sunshine Strips

1) Which item has a lid?

2) Which item has a bell?

3) Point to the covered pot.

4) Which item has a dial with red numbers?

5) Which item has handles?

6) Which item is black?

7) Point to the kitchen timer.

1) Point to the picnic basket.

2) Which item would you use to mash potatoes?

3) Which item is made of metal?

4) How many handles does the picnic basket have?

5) Point to the masher.

6) Which item is silver?

7) Which item would you pack a lunch into?

1) Which item would you use to mix a cake?

2) Which item will measure out a teaspoon of sugar?

3) How many measuring spoons are in this picture?

4) Which item has beaters?

5) Point to the blue item.

6) Is a mixer heavier than measuring spoons?

7) Point to the measuring spoons.

FLASH CARDS (Cut along dotted lines.)

Toaster

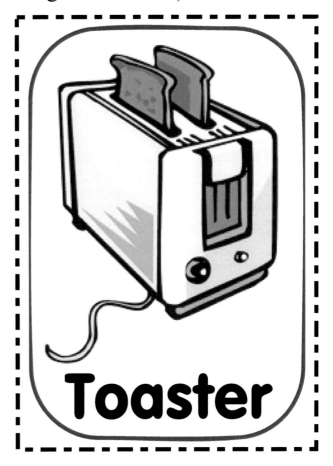

Toaster

Comb

Comb

Pot

Pot

Trash Can

Trash Can

Cut out and award!

117

Grocery List

CANNED FOODS
- ☐ Beans
- ☐ Corn
- ☐ Peas
- ☐ Tomatoes
- ☐ Tomato Sauce
- ☐ Tomato Paste
- ☐ Tuna Fish
- ☐ Mixed Fruit
- ☐ Pineapple
- ☐ Pears
- ☐ Applesauce
- ☐ _____
- ☐ _____

SOUPS
- ☐ Cream of Chicken
- ☐ Cream of Mushroom
- ☐ Broth
- ☐ Chicken Noodle
- ☐ Vegetable
- ☐ Tomato
- ☐ _____
- ☐ _____

SNACKS
- ☐ Cookies
- ☐ Crackers
- ☐ Nuts
- ☐ Popcorn
- ☐ Potato Chips
- ☐ Pretzels
- ☐ _____
- ☐ _____

BAKING GOODS
- ☐ Baking Powder
- ☐ Brown Sugar
- ☐ White Sugar
- ☐ Flour
- ☐ Cake Mix
- ☐ Cake Frosting
- ☐ Brownie Mix
- ☐ Gelatin
- ☐ Pudding
- ☐ Chocolate Chips
- ☐ Marshmallows
- ☐ _____
- ☐ _____

MEXICAN FOODS
- ☐ Green Chiles
- ☐ Refried Beans
- ☐ Taco Shells
- ☐ Salsa
- ☐ Enchilada Sauce
- ☐ _____

FRESH FRUITS
- ☐ Apples
- ☐ Bananas
- ☐ Berries
- ☐ Grapes
- ☐ Melons
- ☐ Oranges
- ☐ Peaches
- ☐ Watermelon
- ☐ Cantaloupe
- ☐ Pears
- ☐ _____
- ☐ _____

FRESH VEGETABLES
- ☐ Broccoli
- ☐ Green Onions
- ☐ Lettuce
- ☐ Cabbage
- ☐ Carrots
- ☐ Celery
- ☐ Cucumbers
- ☐ Garlic
- ☐ Mushrooms
- ☐ Onions
- ☐ Bell Peppers
- ☐ Potatoes
- ☐ Spinach
- ☐ Tomatoes
- ☐ Zucchini
- ☐ _____
- ☐ _____

FROZEN FOODS
- ☐ Vegetable: _____
- ☐ Vegetable: _____
- ☐ Frozen Juice
- ☐ French Fries
- ☐ Hash Browns
- ☐ Pizza
- ☐ TV Dinners
- ☐ Ice Cream
- ☐ _____
- ☐ _____

DAIRY
- ☐ Milk
- ☐ Eggs
- ☐ Butter/Margarine
- ☐ Cottage Cheese
- ☐ Cream Cheese
- ☐ Cheese Slices
- ☐ Shredded Cheese
- ☐ Sour Cream
- ☐ Yogurt
- ☐ _____
- ☐ _____

SPICES/CONDIMENTS
- ☐ Ketchup
- ☐ BBQ Sauce
- ☐ Mayonnaise
- ☐ Mustard
- ☐ Peanut Butter
- ☐ Jam/Jelly
- ☐ Soy Sauce
- ☐ Olive Oil
- ☐ Vegetable Oil
- ☐ Pickles
- ☐ Spice: _____
- ☐ Spice: _____
- ☐ _____
- ☐ _____

SALAD DRESSINGS
- ☐ French
- ☐ Italian
- ☐ Ranch
- ☐ Thousand Island
- ☐ _____
- ☐ _____

MEAT
- ☐ Ground Beef
- ☐ Roast Beef
- ☐ Steak
- ☐ Chicken
- ☐ Ham
- ☐ Bacon
- ☐ Pork Chops
- ☐ Pork Roast
- ☐ Sausage
- ☐ Hot Dogs
- ☐ _____
- ☐ _____

DELI
- ☐ Ham
- ☐ Roast Beef
- ☐ Turkey
- ☐ Pastrami
- ☐ Cheese
- ☐ _____
- ☐ _____

BREAD
- ☐ Sandwich Bread
- ☐ English Muffins
- ☐ Bagels
- ☐ French Bread
- ☐ Tortillas
- ☐ Hamburger/Hot Dog
- ☐ Buns
- ☐ _____
- ☐ _____

Grocery List

BREAKFAST FOODS
- ☐ Oatmeal
- ☐ Cereal _____
- ☐ Cereal _____
- ☐ Pancake Mix
- ☐ Pancake Syrup
- ☐ Granola Bars
- ☐ Coffee
- ☐ Tea
- ☐ _____
- ☐ _____

PASTA/STUFFING/
RICE/POTATOES
- ☐ Macaroni & Cheese
- ☐ Spaghetti
- ☐ Spaghetti Sauce
- ☐ Other pasta: _____
- ☐ Bread Crumbs
- ☐ Stuffing Mix
- ☐ Rice
- ☐ Instant Potatoes
- ☐ _____
- ☐ _____

BEVERAGES
- ☐ Bottled Juice
- ☐ Soda Pop
- ☐ Bottled Water
- ☐ Beer
- ☐ Wine
- ☐ _____
- ☐ _____

PAPER GOODS
- ☐ Paper Towels
- ☐ Napkins
- ☐ Storage Bags - Small
- ☐ Storage Bags - Large
- ☐ Plastic Wrap
- ☐ Foil
- ☐ Kitchen Trash Bags
- ☐ Outdoor Trash Bags
- ☐ Toilet Paper
- ☐ Paper Plates
- ☐ Kleenex
- ☐ _____
- ☐ _____

PET FOODS
- ☐ Dog Food
- ☐ Cat Food
- ☐ Treats
- ☐ Kitty Litter
- ☐ _____
- ☐ _____

CLEANING SUPPLIES
- ☐ Laundry Detergent
- ☐ Fabric Softener
- ☐ Stain Remover
- ☐ Bleach
- ☐ Sponges
- ☐ Dish Detergent
- ☐ Dishwasher Detergent
- ☐ Toilet Bowl Cleaner
- ☐ Glass Cleaner
- ☐ Bathroom Cleaner
- ☐ Furniture Polish
- ☐ Deodorizer
- ☐ _____
- ☐ _____

PERSONAL HYGIENE
- ☐ Toothpaste
- ☐ Dental Floss
- ☐ Shampoo
- ☐ Conditioner
- ☐ Deodorant
- ☐ Razor Blades
- ☐ Shaving Cream
- ☐ Cotton Swabs
- ☐ Bar Soap
- ☐ Lotion
- ☐ _____
- ☐ _____

WELLNESS
- ☐ Vitamins
- ☐ Aspirin
- ☐ Cold Medicine
- ☐ Pain Medicine
- ☐ Flu Medicine
- ☐ Bandages
- ☐ Prescriptions
- ☐ _____
- ☐ _____
- ☐ _____
- ☐ _____
- ☐ _____
- ☐ _____
- ☐ _____
- ☐ _____
- ☐ _____
- ☐ _____
- ☐ _____
- ☐ _____
- ☐ _____
- ☐ _____
- ☐ _____
- ☐ _____
- ☐ _____

OTHER
- ☐ Newspaper
- ☐ Greeting Cards
- ☐ Magazine
- ☐ Batteries
- ☐ Fresh Flowers
- ☐ Film
- ☐ _____
- ☐ _____
- ☐ _____
- ☐ _____
- ☐ _____
- ☐ _____
- ☐ _____
- ☐ _____
- ☐ _____
- ☐ _____
- ☐ _____
- ☐ _____
- ☐ _____
- ☐ _____
- ☐ _____
- ☐ _____
- ☐ _____
- ☐ _____

Notes: _____

_____

_____

_____

_____

_____

_____

_____

_____

_____

_____

_____

_____

Notes: _____

_____

_____

_____

_____

_____

_____

_____

_____

_____

_____

_____

_____

IN CASE OF EMERGENCY

Emergency Information for: _____

Name of Primary Care Doctor: _____ Phone: (____)_____

Hospital Preference: _____

Primary Insurance: _____Member ID: _____

Secondary Insurance: _____Member ID: _____

Food Allergies:

_____
_____

Drug Allergies:

_____
_____

EMERGENCY CONTACTS

Name	Relationship	Phone Number	City and State
		( )	
		( )	
		( )	
		( )	
		( )	
		( )	

Living Will or Healthcare Power of Attorney? (circle one)   Yes   No
Location of the document:_____
Healthcare Power of Attorney's name and phone number: _____

_____

Current Medical Conditions:

_____
_____
_____
_____

Major Surgeries and Dates:

_____
_____
_____
_____

MEDICATIONS I AM TAKING:

Medication Name	Reason for taking this medication:	Dosage	How many times a day	Prescribed by: (Doctor's name and telephone number)

Credits

This book was designed using Art Explosion Publisher Pro by Nova Development.

Photographs used in the "Let's Talk About the Picture" activities are courtesy of Dreamstime.com:

> African Elephant by Francois Etienne Du Plessis, Pretoria, South Africa
> Taj Mahal by Peter Hazlett, London, UK
> Plymouth Lighthouse by Denis Tangney, Chicopee, US

Other photographs used in this book were obtained from PhotoObjects.com, ©2007 JupiterImages Corporation.

Graphics used in this book were obtained from the following sources:

> www.clipart.com, ©2007 JupiterImages Corporation
> www.graphicsfactory.com, a subsidiary of Clip Art Inc.
> Art Explosion Publisher Pro

Order More Sunshine and Joy Books

***To order with a credit card, go to our website at www.sunshineandjoy.com or call 817-788-8490. To order with a check or money order, complete this form and mail it to:

> **Sunshine & Joy**
> **PO Box 872**
> **Bedford, TX 76095-0872**

Quantity

- Big Book of Alzheimer's Activities, Volume 1 ☐
- Big Book of Alzheimer's Activities, Volume 2 ☐

Total Number of Books Ordered: ☐ x $29.95 = ☐

Shipping: $7.50

Subtotal: ☐

Add 8.25% Sales Tax if shipped to a Texas address: ☐

Order Total: ☐

Please make check or money order payable to "Sunshine and Joy"

Buyer Info:

Name: _____

Address: _____

City: _____ State: _____ Zip: _____

Ship To: ☐ Check here if same as above

Name: _____

Address: _____

City: _____ State: _____ Zip: _____